W7-AKY-025

D0064658

BOX 66, SUMAC LANE

Other Books by Edna Hong

The Way of the Sacred Tree
Forgiveness Is a Work as Well as a Grace
Bright Valley of Love
Wild, Blue Berries: A Mystery Novel
Pulu Did It!

BOX 66, SUMAC LANE

A LIVELY CORRESPONDENCE ON SIN AND SANCTITY

Edna Hong

1817

HARPER & ROW, PUBLISHERS, SAN FRANCISCO

New York, Grand Rapids, Philadelphia, St. Louis
London, Singapore, Sydney, Tokyo

To my partner
of fifty-one years

BOX 66, SUMAC LANE. Copyright ©1989 by Edna Hong. All rights reserved. Printed in the United States of America. No part of this book may be used or reproduced in any manner whatsoever without written permission except in the case of brief quotations embodied in critical articles and reviews. For information address Harper & Row, Publishers, Inc., 10 East 53rd Street, New York, NY 10022.

FIRST EDITION

Library of Congress Cataloging-in-Pubication Data

Hong, Edna Hatlestad, 1913–
  Box 66 Sumac Lane.

    I. Title.   II. Title: Lively correspondence on sin and sanctity.
PS3515.04974B6   1989   813'.54   88-46005
ISBN 0-06-250387-1

89   90   91   92   93   RRD   10 9 8 7 6 5 4 3 2 1

Preface

In the following pages I have tried to create a lively and engaging correspondence between an author whose manuscript on sanctification has been rejected and the editor who rejected it, soon including (unbeknown to him) the latter's long-time secretary. Always pertinent, although at times pleasantly impertinent, these letters written over a year between two All Saints' Days explore the existential meaning of the doctrine of sanctification.

These three correspondents are freed from some misconceptions they share with the present and past ages. At the same time they discern the abuses that have placed the doctrine in eclipse and resulted in its becoming the Church's best-kept secret. The scrutiny of the doctrine becomes a mordant but never morbid self-scrutiny. It, of course, cannot help but scrutinize the present age, which seems to be saying yes to self-indulgence and no to abstinence, yes to reprobates and no to saints, yes to sin and no to sanctification. I have tried to infuse in the letters a perspicacity that steers clear of crabbed criticism, never losing sight of the truth that the human condition has remained more or less the same since the first recorded fratricide.

The author of the rejected manuscript, Molly Mortensen, Kierkegaard devotee and translator, and Tate Kuhlman, the editor and Luther expert who rejected the manuscript, exchange quotations to bolster their respective arguments without suffering book or reader the drag of scholarly ballast. The self-irony, humor, and sensitivity of the three correspondents rescue it from the fate that sinks many a book that undertakes to diagnose the human condition and elucidate religious truths. Here the truths of the spirit are not afraid to laugh. Indeed, I hope they dance across the page.

All Saints' Day

Box 66, Sumac Lane
Flutereed, Minnesota

Emmaus Press
4 Willow Lane
Rocky Point, Mass.

Dear Sirs:

Under separate cover you will receive in the postal service's due time a manuscript entitled "Called to Be Saints Alive." By me, the undersigned, who also encloses a self-addressed and stamped envelope for its return should you consider it unworthy of publication.

Sincerely yours,

Molly Mortensen

1

January 4

Emmaus Press
4 Willow Lane
Rocky Point, Mass.

Molly Mortensen
Box 66, Sumac Lane
Flutereed, Minnesota

Dear Ms. Mortensen:

Our staff has carefully scrutinized your manuscript "Called to Be Saints Alive." We all agree that it has much merit, but our market researchers are convinced that the book will not sell. The subject matter has little appeal today. Sanctification does not seem to be an aspiration of the present generation. Regrettably, the modern mind finds the dogma somewhat antiquated. Moreover, the word "saint" has become more or less meaningless in the modern world. On the one hand, the traditional idea of the saint as a spiritual aristocrat does not fit into a democratic society. On the other, we Protestants have pretty well emasculated the idea of the saint.

We are returning your manuscript, but encourage you to submit future manuscripts to us should you apply your impressive writing skills to the present-day needs of our readers.

Sincerely,

Tate Kuhlman
Director, Book Development

TK:mh

January 11

Box 66, Sumac Lane
Flutereed, Minnesota

Mr. Tate Kuhlman
Director, Book Development
Emmaus Press
4 Willow Lane
Rocky Point, Mass.

Dear Mr. Kuhlman:

One presumably should not be surprised to find a Church Press
lentitudinous—that is, take a quarter of a liturgical year to read
and reject a manuscript of 110 pages. But one hardly expects a
Church Press to be so latitudinous that it wants to flush away a
strong doctrine of the Christian faith! Indeed, one—who invented that non-person word "one" from which all the human
blood has been leeched? It could not have been invented in
heaven on high; it must have been invented in hell below! Shall
we start all over again?

I (that is, I, Molly Mortensen, 60 years old, widow, mother of
six, grandmother of ten grandchildren and four granddogs—one
grand and beautiful dog of my own, Emma, an elderly red set-
ter/labrador dog, and Ole, a neutered but not especially neutral
cat—very prejudiced to me; thus with a well-seasoned immuni-
ty to jars and jolts) am not surprised, Mr. Kuhlman (whoever
you are) at your lateishness, but I am surprised—no, shocked!—
at your apparent slavishness. Sir, do you realize that you are a
captive—in captivity to the worst of oppressors, the demands of
the times? Because people nowadays want to feel good about
themselves, want to feel successful, want to know how to cope

3

(with the times!), they demand books that will make them feel good about themselves, feel successful, feel able to cope. So Church Presses (Emmaus Press among them) fall in line and supply books that make people feel good about themselves, feel successful, feel able to cope. (Coping may be a fine humanistic virtue, but it sure isn't a Christian virtue!)—In short, people today don't want to feel uncomfortable. They want a religion they can live with. Which makes me decidedly uncomfortable— I cannot live with that!

What about God's demand? What about his clear call to grow into the fullness of the Son he sent to make us free? Free for what? To conform to the demands of the times?? What about the New Testament's clear call to be sanctified in Christ? Saints alive, Mr. Kuhlman, don't make yourself and Emmaus Press and the Church guilty of plugging our lay-ears with wax (marketable, of course!) so that we no longer hear that call. As for what you said about saints, I'm still so angry that if I tried to write about that my pen would bite the page.

Sincerely, very much so!

Molly Mortensen

P.S.[1] Thank you for returning the manuscript. Since it seems to be about a dead subject, a dying doctrine, I suppose it must be presumed to be also dead or dying. I shall hold a private funeral and entomb it on a shelf in the closet where I keep other out-moded things I cannot bear to throw away, such as the old black hymnbook and a motheaten plaid wool skirt I wore out on a summer tandem trip through Europe with my husband.

P.S.[2] Incidentally, I prefer Mrs. to Mizzzz. Ms. sounds like a bluebottle fly trapped in a Mason jar. (Mason jars are old-fashioned and obsolete, but the times are once again demanding them and paying high prices for them. Do you suppose that the old-fashioned doctrine of sanctification can have a similar comeback? Perhaps replace the doctrine of self-gratification the times have demanded—and gotten with a vengeance. Aha, that's it! The doctrine of self-gratification is in revenge for our scuttling the doctrine of sanctification!)

January 18

Emmaus Press
4 Willow Lane
Rocky Point, Mass.

Molly Mortensen
Box 66, Sumac Lane
Flutereed, Minnesota

Dear Mrs. Mortensen:

Your letter of January 11 has been passed around to the staff at Emmaus Press, and we all feel properly and orthodoxly scolded—but becomingly. You have a gift of scolding that only one other person in my acquaintance has or had: my mother. Her scoldings were never downcasting, always upbuilding. So we thank you for dressing us up instead of down.

However, we all, or the majority of us, agree that the Christian Church in its proclamation of the Gospel, and that includes Church presses, should keep in touch with the times. Do you not agree that the number of persons well-instructed in Christian doctrine has rapidly diminished and that the terminology of faith that is very familiar and almost sacrosanct to an older generation has become meaningless ecclesiastical jargon to a younger generation? Should the Church in its proclamation of the Gospel make itself guilty of the idolatry of words to the neglect of meanings?

I do sincerely regret writing in my letter that "our market researchers are convinced that the book will not sell." I confess that salability often does decide whether or not we publish a book, but I blush to say it. I should have written, "We fear that the book will speak only to those to whom the doctrines and the terminology of the Christian faith are dear familiars, who know them by heart. It will not reach or touch those for whom the doctrines and terminology of the Christian faith may obscure or even distort what the Gospel means."

Please know that we at Emmaus Press appreciate your comments, as we hope and trust that you will appreciate ours.

Sincerely,

Tate Kuhlman

TK:mh

Box 66, Sumac Lane
Flutereed, Minnesota

Dear Tate Kuhlman:

You do not mind, I hope, that I drop the heading. You oughtn't
to. You of all people don't have to be told repeatedly who you
are, what your title is, the name of your press, its address, etc.!
As for me, I find headings to be headaches. So—away with it.
(Ah, I used five lines to dispense with it!)

I heartily agree with you that the now-generation is dreadful-
ly illiterate about the Bible, Christian doctrine, the terminology of faith, etc. A lot of young people, I fear, know the word
Christ only as a swear word. Others claim to believe in God but
are quick to point out that they are not nuts about him. As for
the Church, they wouldn't be caught dead in it.—Well, maybe
dead!

An experience I once had teaching a seventh-grade Sunday
school class illustrates the point where you and I agree. We
were reading aloud the story of Joseph in Genesis. When we
came to the part where Jacob is handed Joseph's bloody coat of
many colors and the stricken father "rent his clothes," I was
suddenly prompted to stop the reading and ask what the word
"rent" meant. The class was astonished that I thought that they
did not know. Hadn't I heard about renting tuxes for weddings
and formals for parties?

Who knows what they understand by the word "sanctification"! But unlike you (and here I strongly disagree with you), I
am not ready to abandon the word. Or replace it with a brand-
new up-to-date word as often as the Church modernizes its liturgy. Why? Because sanctification, the call to be holy, is as

much a staple element of the Gospel as flour is of bread. It can't be separated. (Believe me, I know whereof I speak. I grind my own wheat and make my own bread. If I have any local fame, it is for my bread.) The call to be holy cannot be divorced from the proclamation of the Gospel. Once upon a Christian time it was not the best-kept secret of the Church. It was declared as clearly as the Apostle Paul, whose conversion is celebrated today, declared it in all his Epistles and never separated our redemption and justification in Christ from the call to live the sanctified life of holiness. "Declare it!" he said. "Declare it again and again! We are called to be saints!"

And you want to abandon the word "sanctification"! Don't you realize that it is not simply abandoning a word, it is abandoning the call that salts all of Scripture? <u>Be holy, for I am holy.</u> <u>Put on the new person!</u> To be Christian is to be encountered and challenged by that call. To be Christian is to wrestle with that call.

And you, Sir, want to discard saints because the times have rejected them! May not the spiritual bankruptcy of the modern age be due in part to the rejection of those citizens of two worlds, those sources of spiritual power and often of social reform? I am not one to hurl Bible verses at people in my letters, but may I invite you to look at the first verse in Paul's letters and note that they are addressed "To the saints who are in Christ Jesus. . . . "

Oof, I'm sorry! Now I probably sound to you like a shrill and scolding Zantippe, no longer like your mother. I must seal this and stamp it and drive to the post office and mail it. If I keep it until tomorrow I'll repent of writing it and burn it. But I don't want to repent!

Unrepentantly yours,

Molly Mortensen

February 1

Emmaus Press
4 Willow Lane
Rocky Point, Mass.

Dear Molly Mortensen:

Your second dressing-up letter arrived this morning, and I hasten to answer it to assure you that it was not at all Zantippian shrill. My mother, if she were alive to read it, would nod vigorously and say, "Gut! Gut! You had it coming, Son!" Where you say "Oof!" she would say, "Ach du Lieber!" By the way, does the "Oof" tell us that you are of Norwegian descent? Then let this Norwegian proverb reassure you if I do not: "The word that lies nearest to the heart comes first to the lips." In your case, the pen. Please do not repent of honest convictions. May I say that your convictions about sanctification and saints are coming through in your letters more cogently and vividly than in your manuscript, where they at times were gruminous, like undigested food. Perhaps you should have another go at it?

You are quite right that the doctrine of sanctification is the best-kept secret in the Protestant Church. But you are wrong to think that my colleagues and I wish to keep it hidden or to abolish it altogether. We simply have some fears that in raising it up out of oblivion all the old abuses of that doctrine will rear up again: pride, work-righteousness, separatism, sectarianism, perfectionism, self-glorification, bigotry, spiritual extremism. You will, I am sure, admit that of all the doctrines of the Christian Church the doctrine of sanctification has been the most abused and misused. Is this perhaps why it was swept under the rug? As for the saints, will you not admit that there was a lot of negativ-

10

ism, sentimentalism, and superstition as well as misguided asceticism and moralism intermingled with their admittedly splendid virtues and saintly piety?

Sincerely,

Tate Kuhlman

TK:mh

February 5

601 Oak Street, Apt. 10
Rocky Point, Mass.

Molly Mortensen
Box 66, Sumac Lane
Flutereed, Minnesota

Dear Mrs. Mortensen:

Please do not tell Mr. Kuhlman that I am writing to you, and if
you answer this letter (if you are too busy, I will understand!)
do not write to Emmaus Press. I am Mr. Kuhlman's secretary
and have held that position for twenty years. I like and respect
him very much. He is the best boss a woman could have, but he
is very liberal and I do not always agree with him. However, I
do not let him know that and hope that you will honor my re-
quest not to betray that I have written to you.

You are absolutely right, Mrs. Mortensen, in your battle to
restore sanctification to its rightful place. It certainly has not
been in favor in this century, and I am convinced that this is
why the present generation is so shockingly immoral. It is almost impossible to find a decent movie or book or TV show today! And the goings-on of young people today! I am sure it is
because they never heard the call to be pure and holy that you
wrote about in your manuscript. If I had had any say, it would
not have been rejected!

I just want you to know that I am behind you, and I encourage you to keep on trying to open Mr. Kuhlman's eyes to the
glaring fact that all the immorality in the world today is directly related to the neglect of the doctrine of sanctification.

Thank you for your campaign to raise the standard of purity and holiness again!

Your Truly,

Martha Hoffman

February 8
St. Jerome Emiliani
(not St. Jerome, alias
Eusebius Sophronius
Hieronymus, who
wrote against Joannen
Hierosholymitanium).

Dear Tate Kuhlman:

This time I am abandoning <u>my</u> address. Forms have purpose, but when they become repetitious formalities they are like hobbles on a horse and prevent galloping into a subject.

To gallop forthwith into the subject: The major premise in Christianity, says Kierkegaard, is Jesus Christ, the only name that satisfies the human longing to know the eternal, to define God. The minor premise, says he, is the very thing that Lutheranism partially wiped out with its emphasis on grace alone: a changed life, following Christ, discipleship, hearing and obeying Christ's call. Out of gratitude for the gift of grace, in sheer thankfulness to God, striving to become what we already are by means of the first premise. And that, Mr. Tate, is sanctification. Of course, we can't do it alone, so God sends us his Holy Spirit, who does the real work of making us what we already are by the grace of God and his Son Jesus Christ.

You are so right about the dangers. There is always danger that some crackpot will come along and try to make the minor premise the major premise, but God doesn't run scared. He can always raise up an Augustine, a Francis of Assisi, a Catherine of Siena, a Savonarola, a Martin Luther, a Pascal, a Calvin, a George Fox, a Kierkegaard, a Bonhoeffer, a Mother Theresa, to get the proclamation of the Gospel properly orchestrated and conducted again. Please do not think that I think myself qualified to pick up the conductor's baton, step up on the podium,

14

and get the great symphony that is the Gospel played properly again. But if my little voice can move someone who *is* qualified to orchestrate and conduct the Gospel symphony so that the minor premise, which is so weak and unstressed these days that we do not hear it, is once again heard in its proper relation to the major premise—well, then let it be heard.

But perhaps my voice in my manuscript shouted. Perhaps it was too shrill. Perhaps you were right to reject it. G. K. Chesterton says it requires a saint to write the life of a saint. Likewise, it takes a saint to write a book on sanctification, and I ain't no saint.

No, neither my late husband or I are of Norwegian descent. If we were, the name would be Martenson. Our grandfathers came from the little country that Søren Kierkegaard was proud to call his native land.

Now ponder this (Kierkegaard again!): It is harder for a born and baptized Christian to become a Christian than for a non-Christian.

Sincerely,

Molly Mortensen

February 12

Box 66, Sumac Lane
Flutereed, Minnesota

Miss Martha Hoffman
601 Oak Street, Apt. 10
Rocky Point, Mass.

Dear Miss Hoffman,

Thank you for your letter, the first letter I have ever received from a person whose small initials appear after the colon that punctuates the sender's capital letter initials. I no longer have to wonder who the mh is who types Mr. Kuhlman's letters.

I am happy that you consider Mr. Kuhlman to be the best boss a woman can have, and I assure you that I will not betray that you have written to me concerning the little epistolary discussion of sanctification he and I are carrying on.

I treasure your good letter—good because it so marvelously showed me what is wrong with the manuscript Emmaus Press rejected. It is too negative! Too smug! Too sniping! Your letter helped me to see that sanctification should be presented as the greatest and most exciting adventure in the Christian life. Accepting Christ as our Savior is the prologue. Christ has finished <u>his</u> drama of redemption. Now <u>our</u> drama begins. Now the action begins for us. Now commences the adventure of becoming what he has made us—saints alive!

How can I thank you for showing me so clearly in your letter where I went wrong and what I must do.

Sincerely,

Molly Mortensen

February 15
Day assigned for the
observance of George
Washington's birthday.
I wonder why?
Why rob him of his birthdate?

Dear Molly (that is, if you will write "Dear Tate," which I am certain you will, since you seem to relish discarding proprieties when they become stale. I would like to be Peter Rabbit, sit behind the rhubarb, and watch the weeds fly when you garden. You would make a marvelous editor. Any chance we could get you on the weeding staff here at Emmaus Press?):

This is not a job offer, Molly. We are all of one mind here on Willow Lane—you must stick to writing. To our dismay your last letter expressed some unconfidence in your manuscript. May your unconfidence not sink into the abyss of unself-confidence. Will it help to tell you that your manuscript arrived at Emmaus Press on the crest of a wave of "How to Have a Successful Spiritual Life" mss., most of them written by people who cannot even succeed in writing a book? Then, too, our younger staff, more or less illiterate when it comes to creed and dogma and woefully ignorant about the doctrine of sanctification, promptly renamed it the doctrine of sanctimoniousness. Your manuscript did not have a chance! Well, your letters are so clarifying and illuminating that our chagrined and repentant staff wants you to send the manuscript back and let us look at it again.

So you read Kierkegaard. Maybe you can explain existentialism (which he is supposed to be the father of) to me. No one has yet explained it to me to my satisfaction. May I say that the

17

taste you give me of him in your letters led me to order the seven-volume set of his <u>Journals and Papers</u>. You of course know what the set costs, so you must also know that your tidbit of that Dane was indeed appetizing.

Incidentally, how did that Chinese husband-and-wife translating team ever become involved translating Danish into English?

Sincerely,

Tate

Dear Tate,

NO!!!!!!

No, I will not re-submit "Called to Be Saints Alive!"
I am not being either unconfident or unself-confident when I say that I now perceive it as negative, self-righteous, didactic, censorious, sniping, at times sneering, term-paperish, supercilious, squint-eyedish, hideboundish, dullish, and every conceivable Ish I can think of!

Mulishly yours,

Molly

P.S. Whatever happened to mh, the secretary who typed your letters? I hope to heaven that you have not fired her!? I have had such fun giving her a name: Mable Henderson? Marianne Hackenheimer? Melba Homestead? Martha Hopkins? Myra Hoffman? Did I come close?

February 19

601 Oak Street, Apt. 10
Rocky Point, Mass.

Molly Mortensen
Box 66, Sumac Lane
Flutereed, Minnesota

Dear Mrs. Mortensen:

For the life of me I cannot figure out how my letter could be so helpful, but I am very glad to be of help in your battle for the moral improvement of the present generation. Paul's description of the lusts of the pagans in his day fits the present generation perfectly, don't you think?

Romans 1:28–32. "And even as they did not like to retain God in their knowledge, God gave them over to a reprobate mind, to do those things which are not convenient; being filled with all unrighteousness, fornication, wickedness, covetousness, maliciousness; full of envy, murder, debate, deceit, malignity; whisperers, backbiters, haters of God, despiteful, proud, boasters, inventors of evil things, disobedient to parents. Without understanding, covenant-breakers, without natural affection, implacably unmerciful: who, knowing the judgment of God, that they which commit such things are worthy of death, not only do the same, but have pleasure in them that do them."

I will not quote all the passages about homosexuality and all the other lusts and passions and perversions Paul wrote about. If you want me to give you the chapters and verses, I will. People today are just as much slaves of sin as they were in Paul's day, don't you think? It's Sodom and Gomorrah all over again. The wages of sin is death, so your battle to raise up the doctrine of sanctification is of vital importance. It's a real rescue mission, and I'm proud to be able to help you.

I guess Mr. Kuhlman is not writing any more letters to you, but I would like very much to continue writing to you—that is, of course, if you wish me to.

Yours Truly,

Martha Hoffman

February 22
George Washington's real birthday.

Dear Mulish Molly,*

No, I have not fired mh (Martha Hoffman. You were pretty
close in your name game). I would be a fool to dismiss so "faith-
ful a servant," which she indeed considers herself to be. I fear
that she regards me as her lord and master and herself as a faith-
ful servant, but I cannot make her over and would hurt her if I
spurned all the lovely homage and service "she renders me."
However, the mh will no longer be at the end of my letters. I am
so enjoying writing to you unofficially that I would rather write
my own letters.
    Now, what is existentialism?

                                              Sincerely,

                                              Tate

* Not really! I rather think of you as marvelous, mirthful, mala-
pert Molly.

P.S. My home address, if you care to use it, is: 10 Wildwood
Lane, Rocky Point, Mass.

Ponder this: If a person holds Scripture in one hand, he or she
has to hold the daily newspaper in the other. (Kierkegaard did
not say that.)

February 26

Box 66, Sumac Lane
Flutereed, Minnesota

Martha Hoffman
601 Oak Street, Apt. 10
Rocky Point, Mass.

Dear Miss Hoffman,

Thank you again for a very helpful letter. But if we are going to continue writing to each other, why don't we drop all the formalities? Let's be Martha and Molly to each other. Okay?

Whenever I read Paul's castigations (he certainly did not mince words, did he!), I turn to Peter, who starts out his second letter by writing: "By his divine power, he has given us all the things that we need for life and for true devotion, bringing us to know God himself, who has called us by his own glory and goodness. In making these gifts, he has given us the guarantee of something very great and wonderful to come: through them you will be able to share the divine nature and to escape corruption in a world that is sunk in vice. But to attain this, you will have to do your utmost yourselves, adding goodness to the faith that you have, understanding to your goodness, self-control to your understanding, patience to your self-control, true devotion to your patience, kindness toward your fellow men to your devotion, and, to this kindness, love. If you have a generous supply of these, they will not leave you ineffectual or unproductive: they will bring you to a real knowledge of our Lord Jesus Christ. But without them a man is blind or else short-sighted; he has forgotten how the past sins were washed away. Brothers, you have been called and chosen: work all the harder to justify it. If you

23

do all these things there is no danger that you will ever fall away. In this way you will be granted admittance into the eternal kingdom of our Lord and savior Jesus Christ."

You see, Martha, I like to think of sanctification as the happy road to heaven on which our Savior Jesus Christ has placed us. I also like to think with St. Theresa that "All the way to heaven is heaven." It seems to me that Peter weaves all this into that tight and wonderful paragraph in his second letter.

I am sure that you have heard lots of preaching in your life, Martha. To whom would you rather listen: a preacher who vividly, oh, so vividly, describes our world that is "sunk in vice"— or a preacher who describes the way of sanctification as the way to "something great and wonderful to come"? Which preacher "quickens"? (Isn't that a quaint, old-fashioned but wonderful word? I memorized it when I had to recite the Catechism letter-perfect to my mother, but I did not understand it until I felt my first baby "quicken" in my womb.)

I am already looking forward to your next letter!

Sincerely,

Molly

Dear Tate,

You are going to reconsider and call me Mulish Molly in dead earnest when I stubbornly stick to the theme of sanctification and maintain that the existentialism Kierkegaard fathered is plain and simple sanctification. I am sure that statement would horrify most philosophers and some theologians, but they won't ever know anyway, and you won't tell, will you?

Kierkegaard does not use the term "existentialism." If you will look at the categories alphabetized in the volumes of his Journals and Papers, which you now own, you will find "Exist, Existence, Existential," but there is no "ism" tacked on. When he says, "Our age has completely forgotten what it means to exist," he uses the word in its original Latin meaning—to stand forth. He means a life that is more than we mean when we say "merely existing." As he uses the term, it is qualitative, not factual. He loads the word with his own meaning. For him it means to exist in what one understands, to exist in the truth one understands.

For Kierkegaard, for Christians, Christ is the truth, and to exist in the truth is to exist in Christ, to follow Christ, to walk the Way. You know, of course, that the earliest Christians were called "followers of the Way." (Forgive me if I sound teacher-ish, but you asked for it! Kierkegaard was terribly hard on lec-turers—lecturing professors and assistant professors, lecturing preachers, whose own personal existences did not show that they were existing in the Gospel truth they were proclaiming.)

Methinks I had better shut up! Read him and let him speak for himself.

> Not a teacher,
> not a preacher,
> not a professor—
>
> Merely Molly

March 3

601 Oak Street, Apt. 10
Rocky Point, Mass.

Dear Mrs. Mortensen:

Please do not be angry with me, but I find it difficult to call you Molly. I was brought up in a formal family. When my mother spoke of my father to anyone, she always called him Mr. Hoffman. We never had pet names or nicknames in our family. Then, too, I have been a secretary for twenty years, and I am so used to writing formal letters that it is hard for me to write informally. But please do call me Martha! Mr. Kuhlman does all the time. He asked me to call him Tate, but for the life of me I cannot!

I cannot tell you how thrilled I am that you want to keep on writing to me. It is wonderful to find something beside junk mail in my box.

To answer your question about which preacher I would rather listen to, I think that we have to have both kinds of preachers—the ones who open our eyes to how sunk in sin our generation is, and the ones who show us how to make progress in the kind of Christian life we are supposed to live. I have not read the article (or was it a book?) titled "Whatever Happened to Sin?" But the title caught my eye because it seems that nothing is a sin these days. It seems that the only sin today is to think anything a sin. You never hear anyone preach about the seven deadly sins any more. I wonder if preachers can even name them? I asked Mr. Kuhlman if he could name them. He remembered lust, gluttony, and pride, but he forgot anger, covetousness, envy, and sloth. I myself think there are many more than

26

seven. The apostle Paul lists fifteen in Galatians 5:19–21. But I suppose many of those can be grouped under the seven deadly sins.

I wish now that I had read your sanctification manuscript. I am wondering how you defined sanctification. Isn't it plainly and simply rooting sin out of your life? Please do not rush to answer. I know that you are a very busy woman.

I wish that you and Mr. Kuhlman were still writing to each other. It was very interesting to type his letters to you and file away your answers. I confess that I read them.

Your Truly,

Martha Hoffman

Martha, dear Martha!

You apparently were brought up under LAW and I under GRACE. Grace, all grace! In our home we even used each other's toothbrushes if we couldn't immediately locate our own!—I need you, Martha—the way apple pie needs cheese to cut the cloying sweetness. But maybe you need me, too! So will you be the vinegar in my theology, and let me be the honey in yours? Okay?

One of my favorite authors, Charles Williams, describes better how we two need each other in his book <u>The Descent of the Dove:</u> "The Rigorous view is vital to sanctity; the Relaxed view is vital to sanity. Their union is not impossible, but it is difficult; for whichever is in power begins, after the first five minutes, to maintain itself from bad and unworthy motives. Harshness, pride, resentment encourage the one; indulgence, falsity, detestable good fellowship the other."

You, Martha, are dangerously close to making sanctification a bitter pill, and I, Molly, may be just as close to making it a butterscotch custard. And it seems we both can quote Scripture to support our views! Isn't that always the case? Even the Devil is said to be able to quote Scripture. —Who said that? Is that in Scripture?

To me sanctification is not the negative way, the forbidding, rejecting way, the No-No way. It is the way of the divine YES. In Christ it is always YES, "However many of the promises God made, the Yes to them all is in him" (2 Corinthians 1:20). Neither is sanctification the way of Perfection. I don't even want to call it the Best way! That wonderful Paul (whom we can both quote for support!) says it better than I could ever say it even if I were to be gifted with the most beautiful words. I'm using the translation of <u>The New Testament of the Jerusalem Bible.</u>

". . . I look on everything as so much rubbish if only I can have Christ and be given a place in him. I am no longer trying for perfection that comes from the Law, but I want only the perfection that comes through faith in Christ, and is from God and based on faith."

I love you!

Molly

Dear Professor Molly,

You disclaim being a teacher, preacher, or professor, but if you
are not one of the three you ought to be. You certainly did clear
up for me some of the ambiguities that confuse the word "existentialism." You made it clear that Søren Kierkegaard would
vehemently deny being father of the atheistic existentialism so
current today. Yet I suspect that when I get further into his
<u>Journals and Papers</u> I will discover that he agrees with the non-
Christian existentialists that we human beings are the Big
Question in life, but where they see human life as nauseating or
absurd or hopeless or meaningless, he sees possibility and choice
for us human beings. The easy way is to choose despair, because
that's the way we tilt.

Molly, I read a lot of manuscripts on theological subjects and
try to keep up on what other presses are publishing that pertains
to the Christian faith, but I have not encountered anyone yet
who claims that Christian existentialism is the old-fashioned
doctrine of sanctification. If some learned D.D. attacks you, let
me know. I will put on my helmet and coat of mail and cross
swords with him or her.

If Christian existentialism is to exist in the Christian truth
one knows, then it is indeed sanctification. Would you agree
that the doctrine of sanctification declares that it is impossible
to say "I know" without saying "I live"? It's possible, of course,
but that is not living, or living in the perpetual growing "into
the fullness of Christ." It is not "striving to become what we
already are by the grace of God and his son Jesus Christ."*

You seem to know Kierkegaard pretty well. May I confess a
modest acquaintance with Martin Luther? Please continue to
toss Kierkegaard quotations at me, and I promise to toss back

Luther quotations. Here's one that beautifully sums up what I am trying to say:

> Do not imagine that the life of a Christian is rest and quiet. It is a passage and a progress from vice to virtues, from light to light, from virtue to virtue. And if someone is not in transit, do not think that he is a Christian.

In other words, if one is not on the road of sanctification, one is on the road to spiritual stagnation.

It just hit me like a bolt out of the blue, Molly, that the liturgical year celebrates all this wonderfully. I wonder why I never saw it before. The first half of the year focuses on the life of Christ, what Christ has done and is doing for us in him and through the Holy Spirit. The second half focuses on our response, our grateful growing in grace and holiness day by day. This is what the long, green Trinity season is all about, and it ends just as it should, celebrating saints: All Saints' Day, which we have allowed to be spooked out by Hallow'en. What wise guys those ancient Fathers who planned the Church Year were. Ah, who is lecturing and preaching now?

Yours,

Tate

*Mortensen, Molly. Letter IV, February 8, 1988.

P.S. But (this but is a monster, dear Molly): The problem still remains—how to make holiness as attractive as sex to the common human being. I'm still unconvinced that sanctification is the way.

March 15

601 Oak Street, Apt. 10
Rocky Point, Mass.

Dear Molly,

As you see, I am addressing you by your first name! How can I write "Dear Mrs. Mortensen" to someone who wrote "I love you!" in her last letter? No one has ever said that to me before, except a freckled red-haired boy in fifth grade, but he moved away. Thank you for writing that. I really think you mean it. Otherwise I could not call you Molly. Thank you, too, for saying that you need me and that we need each other. No one tells me that either. I do not see how Mr. Kuhlman could get along without me as his secretary. If you only knew how careless the younger secretaries are! They will not work a minute overtime to finish up letters unless they are paid double. Some of them even refuse to make coffee for their bosses. They say that is not their job. I not only make coffee, I bring cookies or doughnuts at least twice a week. Nice as he is, Mr. Kuhlman does not tell me that he needs me. But he does give me flowers on Secretary Day.

The Divine Yes view of sanctification is new to me, or I had not thought of it before. I shall make it my Search Project in my private Bible Study and Prayer Hour (from 6 A.M. to 7 A.M. every morning). It is a much more appealing view than the negative view—just so I do not get dragged into positive thinking, which to my way of thinking is pretty thin. Did not our Lord—no, it was Paul (1 Thessalonians 4:7)—say, "God has not called us unto uncleanness but unto holiness."

I suppose it is true that to fall into sin is human, but it seems to me that to keep on sinning is devilish. Surely we who call ourselves Christians should be constantly striving for perfection! So how can you say that the Way of Sanctification is not the Way of Perfection and not even "the Best Way"?

Forgive me, Molly, for being so outspoken. I was taught never to disagree with anybody and have made a habit of keeping everything with which I disagree to myself. It certainly is not easy when there is so much to disagree with! But somehow I feel that you will not think less of me if I tell you what I really think. I really do want to know.

I love you, too, Molly Mortensen!

Martha

March 17

St. Patrick's Day

Dear Tate,

Sure, an' to be sure, it was a lovely letter, a grand letter, a dar-
lin' letter you wrote last! Yes, an' thrue, so thrue it was! Amn't I
the lucky wan to have met up with the likes of you! Speakin' for
meself, wud that you were here an' we cud dhrink a cup o' tay
together an' talk o' God an' the Sacred Heart of Jesus an' his
blessed Muther an' saints an' 'specially himself St. Patrick!
Since it canna be, I send you a sprig o' shamrock to please phut
in the Gud Book.

Do you know why the shamrock is the national emblem of
Ireland? St. Patrick (who wasn't an Irishman at all) lived during the time when the Christian doctrine of the Trinity was being threatened by the Arian heresy that Christ was created by
God and was not divine. St. Patrick used the bright green three-
leafed shamrock as a visual aid to explain that the three persons
of the Father, Son, and Holy Spirit unite in one Godhead.

As for St. Patrick in particular and saints in general, it is true,
Tate, that their lives may in some respects be grossly exaggerat-
ed by a public starving for saints. St. Patrick's reputation certainly became inflated by exaggerations. He is reported to have
established 700 churches during the period of his mission to Ireland. That meant one every two weeks! Impossible, of course,
yet his actual and verified missionary work was incredible. St.
Patrick and the true saints had their own private exaggerations,
but they possessed the power to check their own exaggerations.
I am reminded of what Flannery O'Connor said of one of her
characters: "If she hadn't had her faith she would have been the
stinkiest logical positivist that ever lived." Non-Christians do
not have that power, and so we have Hitlers and their un-

34

checked exaggerations. St. Patrick had that power, and it was
Jesus Christ.

Blessings galore!

Molly

P.S. Are you wishin' the woman wud dhry up? Are you won-
derin' why herself is wearin' the green and is full o' St. Patrick
blarney? 'Tis all because herself gave a talk to a flock o' her-
selves at a meetin' the day afther yisterday—that is, the day before tomorrow.

March 28

10 Wildwood Lane
Rocky Point, Mass.

Dear Molly,

In haste. Yesterday the editorial board of Emmaus Press met and faced up to the grim fact that although we are breaking even financially we certainly are not making money. After two hours of painful deliberation, we decided that the only solution was to make some radical changes. Namely:

1. After May 1 our name will cease to be Emmaus Press and we will be known as Pasta Press.
2. Pasta Press will publish recipe books, especially cookbooks compiled by Christian organizations. As well as esthetically pleasing books, we can offer church womens' groups excellent advertising and marketing skills that will make their parochial productions national or even international. Pasta Press will, of course, share the profits with the church groups.
3. Pasta Press will also publish its own creative cookbooks.

Here is where you come in, Molly. Garrison Kiellor has made Minnesota rather famous, and we are convinced that a Minnesota recipe book would be immediately popular. Do you think that you and your friends and relatives and acquaintances could compile such a book as quickly as possible?

What would you think of the title "Minnesota Soul Food"?

Eagerly awaiting your answer,

Tate

April Fools' Day

I am sorry, Sir Tate, to naysay you
But your idea is corn off the cob.
So corny in fact that if it were true
I still would not want the job.

                    Yours, unbefooled!

                    Molly

P.S. If your letter had not come today, I might have been.

                    Also—!
                    Good/Black Friday
                    Golgatha Day

Dear Tate,

How often, I wonder, does April Fools' Day come on Good Friday? A bit incongruous, but perhaps not so inappropriate after
all. Jesus Christ, Son of God, is crucified as a common criminal
on a cross. April Fool! Jesus Christ, God's own Self, is weak and
subject to death like us. And this is supposed to be Gospel! God's
power—weakness! God's power is perfected in weakness! April
Fool!

   Jesus Christ did not write one word about sanctification,
but he came, a blessed fool, to live among us damned fools and
gave us a vision of an upside-down holiness and a topsy-turvy

37

humility hitherto unknown in the human race. Modern theologians would call him the Divine Paradox. The Dakota Indians would call him the heyoka. Do you know about the heyoka, Tate—the contrary, the upside-down Indian who did everything backward?

The ancient Dakota were able to create an explanation for all the phenomena of nature (mice nibbled at and ate up the moon, and thus a new moon was literally a brand-new moon), but they could not explain thunder and lightning. It was an irrational force in nature for which they had no rational explanation and which terrorized them. It was incredible, unpredictable, contradictory, paradoxical. So they created the heyoka figure, whose role in life was to placate this irrational force. To do this, he was obliged to act irrationally. He did everything backward—wore his clothes backward, rode his horse backward, wore little or nothing in the winter and all the clothes he possessed in the summer. When the black thunderclouds towered in the west he walked on moccasined hands around the circle of tents to placate the thunder spirit. A paradoxical figure, the village fool!

Christ, the Paradox, the Fool of God! St. Ephrem, a saint who was also a poet, called him:

> the great one who became small
> the shepherd who became a lamb
> the farmer who became a grain of wheat
> the provider of all who entered and experienced hunger
> the one who gives drink entered and experienced thirst
> the one who clothes all entered naked and
> stripped from the womb.

And what this blessed fool did and does for us no one could put better than another poet, Gerard Manley Hopkins.

In a flash, at a trumpet crash,
I am all at once what Christ is, since he was what I am, and

38

this Jack, joke, poor potsherd, patch, matchwood, immortal
  diamond
Is immortal diamond.

April Fool, Tate! "For God's foolishness is wiser than human
wisdom, and God's weakness is stronger than human strength."
If you have forgotten where that is, it's in 1 Corinthians 1:25.

Yours,

Molly

April 3
Easter Sunday Night

Dear Tate,

I became so excited about the fool symbolism that I forgot to tell you that on this next Wednesday I will begin a Great Circle Tour visiting my scattered children. When I am on a trip, I write only to children and grandchildren and write only "Wish you were here!" cards. On sedentary pilgrimage, as you know too well, I write a volume. Enjoy your vacation from my verbosity. It will last approximately a month.

Grace and Peace,
Molly

P.S. Before I depart, may I ask you a question I have wanted to ask you ever since mh for a brief spell wrote your letters to me. Do you ever tell her that you appreciate her—indeed, need her?

April 3
Easter Sunday Night

Dear Martha,

Did you have a beatitudinous Easter out there in Rocky Point? I had an outwardly quiet one, but inwardly—! I sang "Christ the Lord is risen again!" at our sunrise service in a discreet voice, but my inward voices sang so crescendo that I was afraid that they would disgrace me if the congregation heard them. I thought of Martin Marty's story of the woman who was forbidden by court order to sing in church on Sunday. It seems that she had a grudge against the pastor and sang loudly and deliberately off key!

I'm so happy that you want to be a back-door friend, Martha! My friends come in through the back door of my house, and I never turn my smudged (why is it always across the stomach?) apron around when I see them coming. —I don't know if it is a proverb or not, but it ought to be. "The door to a friend's heart is never locked." Thank you for loving and trusting me enough to take your honest but secret thoughts out of the closet and let me see them. Now I'll open my closet door and let you see my unvarnished thoughts about sanctification as a way of perfection.

I honestly think that the holiness of God is something more than moral perfection. As for moral perfection, why do we Christians one-sidedly consider it to be chastity and aim most of our arrows of judgment and condemnation at the immorality of committing adultery? What about the immorality of sinful intercourse with money and property? What about the immorality of lust for power and prestige and prosperity? What about the obscenity of curdling hope and joy in the lives of those around us? What about the vice of gossip and pious nagging?

I also think that there is something holier than regular

41

church attendance and that there is nothing unholier than the stuffiness of a purely habitual religion. I also think that blacker than the blackest private guilt is the faultily faultless public righteousness that privately is no more than self-righteousness, the self-righteousness of living up to our own human standards of perfection. Of all the dangers lurking along the way of perfection, the most dangerous, it seems to me, is to set up our human standards of perfection and virtue and faithfully and conscientiously live up to them. How weak and amputated they are compared to the nine beatitudes! We sophisticated sinners neglect to examine our virtues and to see them as falling far short of God's standards and requirements—and therefore sinful. St. Augustine said, "The virtues of pagans are glittering vices." Someone else in a similar vein said, "The good is the greatest enemy of the best." Because we pretty well measure up to our own standards of perfection, we feel that we do not really need grace, but we would not be so ungracious as to refuse it. But we do not feel especially grateful for what we think we really don't need. So our response to God's grace becomes, "We really don't need it, thank you," instead of, "Thank you, oh, thank you! Ah, how I need your grace!" And then a striving to do God's will—a striving born of gratitude, not of a do-it-yourself sanctification.

I fear that deep down inside us sophisticated Christians is the feeling, "We are good Christians, and we don't want to become anything better."

Martha, Martha! Dear back-door friend to whom all my closets are open, I'm not writing to you from a lofty feeling of moral superiority to anyone! I more or less measure up to my own standards of moral perfection, but oof, I am monstrously substandard when measured by Christ's standards. Can you tell me why I feel very uneasy with people of no spiritual depth whatever—but equally uneasy with people who have what I consider too much? Why do I want people to be jolly and joyful, but not too-

tootoo? Why am I so confounded proud of being such a modest, humble, and self-sacrificing woman?—You will have a lot of time to ponder my questions, because I will be gone for a month visiting my six children in six different states. So now may I give you a big goodbye hug and slip out your back door?

Love,

Molly

April 10
Second Sunday of Easter

Dear Molly, wherever you are!

Are you having a jolly time with your six children? May I confess that I am jealous? I have none. My wife had diabetes from early childhood and we were advised not to have children, and she became too frail for us to think of adopting. I have been a widower for 20 years. In a way it amuses and pleases me that we know so little about each other, that is, all the "facts" one puts into resumes when applying for jobs. Do you wonder if I am potbellied? Are you short or tall? A bantam weight or a heavyweight? Please don't tell me! I don't care! It's enough for me to know that your mind is weighty and your spirit is not fat. Your spirit literally danced all over your April Fool letter. May I have the next dance? And the next?

But you still have not addressed the "but" with which I ended my letter prior to the silly one. When you read what I am about to write, you will think I have had a spiritual relapse since that letter. So far, Molly, you have been silent about the "fear and trembling" and the horror of self-loathing that it seems to me one must experience when one sees one's own imperfections under the searchlight of holiness. You say nothing about the terror of "dying-to" that Paul talks about so much. How can one help but feel the Good News of the Gospel as Bad News the more progress one makes along the way of sanctification? Progress along that way seems to be going backward!

Moreover, every human being is a human being before he or she is a saint, and being human is laced with pain. Can anyone who has the Bible in one hand and the daily newspaper in the other and reads them both dance a jolly Gospel jig in this vale of tears? Moreover, Molly, can the person leaping and dancing in joy over grace use grace to hang on to his or her money, and still keep progressing on the way of sanctification? Moreover, can the person who chooses to take the risk of sanctified obedience to God's will escape suffering? What do you say to C. S. Lewis's statement in The Problem of Pain: "The problem is not why some humble, pious, believing people suffer, but why some do not."

I'm glad that this letter does not reach you wherever you are with whatever child you are. You will find it when you come back so refreshed in every way that you will not succumb to its dark questions. But I suspect that you would not succumb anyway, because you seem to have a faith that can survive any and every mood. Are you the unsinkable Molly Brown? Can you speak healing truth to this man who still cannot find the way of sanctification very appealing?

Namely,

Tate

P.S. I took your advice and told Martha Hoffman that I did not know what I would do without her, and she was so overwhelmed that she forgot to put cream in my coffee when she brought it to me. I did not want to fluster her more by asking for it, so I drank it black, and to show her how much I appreciated her I ate four of her doughnuts instead of my usual two. No, I am not pot-bellied.

April 10
11 P.M.

Dear Molly,

Every day I wonder where you are and what you are doing and thinking today. Every morning I pray that your plane will not crash and that the sun will shine where you are. I know that you will not receive this letter until you return home, but I simply must write and tell you about my day today!

I know that you did not mean me when you wrote that "there is nothing unholier than a stuffy habitual religion," but I took it to heart. I did not go to church this morning, the first time since I had the flu a year ago. But I felt so guilty and miserable all day that I went to church tonight. The only church that was having an evening service was the Grace Baptist Church, so I went there. I must say it was quite informal. There was no liturgy at all, and the songs were so different I felt like walking out at first, but then I realized it was the fault of my prejudices against anything different, so I stayed. It wasn't long before I was singing along as loudly and joyfully as all the other people. I even clapped along with them! They sang and prayed so much that the sermon was short, but maybe that was because it was an evening meeting and parents of small children had to get them home to bed. After the service lots of people came over to greet me and ask me to come back again. One of the women lives in this very building, apartment 3. She invited me to come to supper tomorrow night after work! One very young woman works as a secretary across the street from Emmaus Press. We are going to eat lunch together some day this week at a vegetarian restaurant downtown. She is a vegetarian. I used to be prejudiced against them, too, but maybe they have their reasons. Anyway, I am going to be open-minded.

Of course I will not stop going to my Lutheran church! In

46

fact, next Sunday I will go to both the 9:00 A.M. Lutheran service and the 7:30 P.M. Baptist service. Now what do you think of that, Molly Mortensen? Does that make me doubly holy or doubly unholy?

It is 11:15 at night now. I did not look at ten o'clock news as I always do and then go right to bed. I telephoned my sister in Florida and talked to her for half an hour.

At first she thought something terrible must have happened to me—like losing my job or wrecking my car. Speaking of my job, Molly, on Friday Mr. Kuhlman told me that he did not see how he could get along without me! It wasn't even Secretary Appreciation Week! He really is a wonderful gentleman, Molly, and since we are back-door friends and our closet doors are open to each other, I will tell you that I have had a crush on him all these years. But I have always known that I did not have a chance. It seems that he is not interested in women. I was hoping that he would keep on writing to you, but he stopped doing that, too. His wife must have been very beautiful and wonderful for him to carry the torch for her all these years.

I have not addressed all the points in your wonderful letter, Molly, but I will write again before you come home and do so. I am thinking about them all the time, even though my mind sometimes aches with the stretching you are forcing it to do!

Love,

Martha

Molly, Molly!

While you are laughing with your children and dandling your grandchildren on your knee (I envy you, Molly, but I do not begrudge you), I am wrestling with Paul's and Søren's and, apparently, your "dying-to" concept. All three of you seem to make it a necessary concomitant to sanctification. It seems to boil down to:

Suffer————or forfeit eternal happiness.
Die to self————or be damned.
Hate your parents————or lose the love of God.
Die to the world————or go to hell.
Die to being human————or lose eternity.

The equation seems to be:

Wretchedness and misery = dying-to = sanctification.

Is this sanctification, Molly? If so, I want none of it! It seems to me to be the theology of the mole, not of the eagle! Die to all that is human? Hate one's self? Damn it, Molly, I love being human. I like myself. And so do you, Molly Mortensen. If you did not, your Christian faith would not dance in your delightful letters as it does. You would have a faith as prissy and prudish and straitlaced and puritanical as my secretary's. Be assured, I am not complaining! It makes her a scrupulously conscientious secretary. She is well-named Martha.

I feel better now that I have this off my chest. Do you know William Blake's poem, "A Poison Tree"?

I was angry with my friend:
I told my wrath, my wrath did end.
I was angry with my foe:
I told it not, my wrath did grow.

Impatiently waiting!

Tate

April 17

Dear Molly,

My, but I do miss your letters! I am counting the days until you come home and will begin writing to me again. I have been puzzling over some other points in your last letter, but before I write about them I would like to report on my trying to do something about "the stuffiness of my purely habitual religion." You did not say that about <u>my</u> religion, Molly. <u>I</u> am saying that.

Well, the Baptist secretary across the street from Emmaus Press came to pick me up for lunch on Thursday, and I introduced her to Mr. Kuhlman and explained how we had met. When I came back, he asked, "Are you going to <u>two</u> churches now?" The way he asked it, I think he thinks that I am becoming fanatic about religion. He would be even more convinced of that if he knew that a Baptist woman (who lives in this building and invited me to supper) and I are starting a Bible Study Group for those living at 601 Oak Street who want one. We are going to call it the Back-door Neighbors' Bible Study, and we are going to be completely open with each other and not pretend to be more pious than we really are.

What do you think of our starting out by trying to understand the relation between sanctification and moral perfection? I really do not see how you can run away from Matthew 5:48: "Be ye therefore perfect, even as your Father which is in heaven is perfect." Jesus himself said that! Also, 1 Peter 1:14–16: "As obedient children, not fashioning yourselves according to the former lusts in your ignorance but as he which hath called you is holy, so be ye holy in all manner of conversation; because it is written, Be ye holy, for I am holy."

I shall bring whatever you write to the first Bible study in May. We have to get organized first. My Baptist friend and I are going together to knock on the apartment doors, because we are too scared to do it alone. Pray for us, Molly!

Love,
Martha

April 29
St. Catherine (of Siena! There are 50
other sainted Catherines, but she is the
most famous.)

Dear Tate,

Came home Wednesday. Took care of bills and notes to the children assuring them that I had arrived home safely and that Emma and my house plants had been well cared for by my neighbor but were in seventh heaven to see me again. Me likewise them! Tonight I am answering some very insistent letters—yours first.

First of all, your secretary's "prissy, prudish faith"!!! How do you know that it is prissy and prudish? Did you ever talk to her about it? Did you ever talk to her as if she were a person and not a word-processing machine? Did you ever take her out to lunch by herself alone? As for being "well-named." Do you think Jesus' friend Martha was all work and no laughter, no tears, no warmth, no longing? Who was the first woman to say to Jesus: "I believe that you are the Christ, the Son of God"? Martha, not Mary!

As for your more pain-full than vehement grilling on the concept of dying-to and its relation to sanctification, oh, Tate, my sometimes too sharp tongue is silent. How often have I not (and still yet!) asked the same questions! I reacted the same way to much of what Kierkegaard says about dying-to in his journals, although it comforted me to hear him say that it is a purely voluntary act, God does not force anyone to do it, and that he himself had not done it fully. Nevertheless, he says, Christianity requires it and the requirement must be heard. It is part of the downward ascent in the relationship with God.

In a small book, For Self-Examination, Kierkegaard wrote much more clearly and far less astringently about dying-to. The

52

book is out of print, but friends of mine have retranslated it and are allowing me to excerpt portions of it and send to you. Please read it through to the marvelous parable and the prayer at the end. I think it will defog the fog. It did for me.

Grace, peace, and clarity,

Molly

(Excerpts from the draft of a retranslation by Howard and Edna Hong of Søren Kierkegaard's For Self-Examination.)

IT IS THE SPIRIT WHO GIVES LIFE

My listener, in connection with Christianity, there is nothing to which every person is by nature more inclined than to take it in vain. Neither is there anything that is at all Christian, not one single Christian qualification that by some slight modification, by removing some more specific middle term, does not become something entirely different, something about which one must say, "This has arisen in the heart of man"—and thus is taken in vain. On the other hand, there is nothing against which Christianity has protected itself with greater vigilance and zeal than against being taken in vain. There is not one, not one Christian qualification into which Christianity does not first of all introduce as the middle term: death, dying-to [at afdøe], in order to protect the essentially Christian from being taken in vain. They say, "Christianity is gentle comfort, is the doctrine of the grounds of gentle comfort." Well, it cannot be denied—that is, if you will first of all die, die-to, but this is not so gentle! They represent Jesus Christ, saying, "Hear his voice—how he calls, gently inviting, all to himself, all those

53

who suffer, and promises to give them rest for their souls. And truly this is so; God forbid that I should say anything else, but yet, yet—before this rest for the soul falls to your lot and in order that it can fall to your lot, it is required that you first of all die, die-to (something the inviter also says, something his whole life on earth expressed every single day and every single hour of the day). Is this so inviting?

Likewise with this Christian teaching: It is the Spirit who gives life. To what feeling does a person cling more firmly than to the feeling of being alive; what does one crave more strongly and violently than really to feel life in oneself; from what does one shrink more than to die! But here a life-giving Spirit is indeed proclaimed. Then let us take hold of it. Who wants to think twice? Bring us life, more life, so that the feeling of being alive might swell in me—as if all life were concentrated in my breast!

But is this supposed to be Christianity, this appalling fallacy? No, no! This life-giving in the Spirit is not a <u>direct</u> heightening of the natural life in a person in <u>immediate</u> continuation from and connection with it—what blasphemy! How horrible to take Christianity in vain this way—it is a new life. A new life, yes, and this is no platitude as, for example, when we use this phrase about this and that every time something new begins to stir in us—no, it is a new life, literally a new life—because, mark this well, death goes in between, dying-to, and a life on the other side of death—yes, that is a new life.

Death goes in between; this is what Christianity teaches, you must die-to. The life-giving Spirit is the very one who slays you; the first thing the life-giving Spirit says is that you must enter into death, that you must die-to—it is this way in order that you may not take Christianity in vain. A life-giving Spirit—that is the invitation; who would not willingly take hold of it! But die first—that is the halt!

It is the Spirit who gives life. Yes, the Spirit gives life—

through death. As it says in an old hymn that wants to comfort the bereaved on the loss of the dead: "With death we life begin," so also, spiritually understood, the communication of the life-giving Spirit begins in death. Think about this festival day [Pentecost]! It was indeed the Spirit who gives life who today was poured out upon the apostles—and the Spirit really was a life-giving spirit; their lives demonstrated this and their deaths, to which testimony is given by the history of the Church, which came into existence precisely because the Spirit who gives life was communicated to the apostles. But what was their condition prior to this? Ah, who has had to learn in the way the apostles did what it means to die to the world and to oneself! For who has nourished such great expectations as in one sense the apostles were prompted to nourish, at least for a while, and whose expectations were disappointed in this way? Then, of course, came Easter morning and Christ arose from the grave, and then came the Ascension—but what more? Yes, he was now taken up into glory—but what more? Do you believe that any human hope, the boldest human hope, dared even in the remotest way to become involved in the task that was assigned to the apostles? No, here every merely human hope must despair. Then came the Spirit who gives life—the apostles were indeed dead, dead to every merely earthly hope, to every human confidence in their own powers or in human assistance.

Therefore, death first; you must first die to every merely earthly hope, to every merely human confidence; you must die to your selfishness, or to the world, because it is only through your selfishness that the world has power over you; if you are dead to your selfishness you are also dead to the world. But naturally there is nothing a human being hangs onto so firmly— indeed, with his whole self!—as to his selfishness! Ah, the separation of soul and body in the hour of death is not as painful as being forced to be separated from one's soul when you are alive! And a human being does not hang onto this physical life as firmly as one's selfishness hangs onto its selfishness! . . .

My listener, I have something more I would like to say, but I shall cast it in a form that at first glance you may find not quite solemn. Yet I do it deliberately and advisedly, for I believe that precisely in this way it will make a truer impression on you.

Once upon a time there was a rich man. At an exorbitant price he had purchased abroad a pair of entirely flawless, splendid horses, which he had wanted for his own pleasure and the pleasure of driving them himself. About a year or two passed by. If anyone who had known these horses earlier now saw him driving them, he would not be able to recognize them: their eyes had become dull and drowsy; their gait lacked style and precision; they had no staying power, no endurance; he could drive them scarcely four miles without having to stop for a rest, and sometimes they came to a standstill just when he was driving his best; moreover, they had acquired all sorts of quirks and bad habits, and although they of course had plenty of feed they grew thinner day by day.

Then he called in the royal coachman. He drove them for a month. In the whole countryside there was not a pair of horses that carried their heads so proudly, whose eyes were so fiery, whose gait was so beautiful; there was no pair of horses that could hold out as they did, running even thirty miles in a stretch without stopping. How did this happen? It is easy to see: the owner, who without being a coachman meddled with being a coachman, drove the horses according to the horses' understanding of what it is to drive; the royal coachman drove them according to a coachman's understanding of what it is to drive.

So also with us human beings. When I think of myself and the countless people I have come to know, I have often said to myself sadly: Here are capacities and talents and qualifications enough, but the coachman is lacking. For a long time now, from generation to generation, we humans have been, if I may put it this way (in order to carry on the metaphor), driven according

56

to the horses' understanding of driving; we are governed, trained, and educated according to mankind's conception of what it is to be a human being. See, because of this we lack elevation and it follows from this in turn that we are able to endure very little. We are impatient and promptly use the means of the moment and impatiently want to see instantly the reward for our work, which for that very reason is not very good.

Things were different once. There was a time when it pleased the deity himself, if I may put in this way, to be the coachman; and he drove the horses according to the coachman's understanding of what it is to drive. Oh, what a person was capable of then!

Ponder the text for today! There sit twelve men, all belonging to the social class we call the common man. Him whom they worshiped as God, their Lord and Master, they have seen crucified. They can be said to have witnessed the loss of everything in a way that can never be said of anyone else, even in the remotest manner. True, he thereupon ascended victorious into heaven—but that of course also means he is gone—and now they are sitting there and waiting for the Spirit to be communicated to them in order that they, cursed by the little nation to which they belong, can proclaim a teaching that will arouse the hatred of the whole world against them. This is the task; these twelve men are supposed to transform the world, and on the most appalling scale, against its will. Here, truly, the understanding comes to a standstill! Even now, long after, in forming a faint conception of it the understanding comes to a halt—if one still has any at all. It is enough to drive one out of one's mind, if one still has any from which to be driven.

This is Christianity, which must get through. And these twelve men carried it through. In one sense, they were men like us, but they were driven well—yes, indeed, they were driven well.

Then came the next generation. They carried Christianity

through. They were men just like us—but they were driven well! Yes, indeed, that they were! They were like that pair of horses when the royal coachman drove them. Never has a human being lifted his head as proudly in elevation over the world as did the first Christians in humility before God! And just as that pair of horses could run if need be thirty miles without pausing to catch their wind, so also did they run; they ran seventy years in a stretch without getting out of the harness, without stopping to rest anywhere. No, proud as they were in their humility before God, they said, "It is not for us to hang back and dawdle along the way; we do not stop—until eternity." That was Christianity, which had to go through, and they carried it through—yes, that they did; but they were also driven well—yes, that they were!

O Holy Spirit—we pray for ourselves and for all people—O Holy Spirit, you who give life, here there is no want of capabilities, education, and sagacity—indeed, there may rather be too much. But what is wanting is that you take away whatever is corrupting to us, that you take power away from us and give life. Certainly a person experiences a shudder like death's shudder when you, in order to become the power in us, take power away from him. Oh, but if even animals at a later moment understand how good it was for them that the royal coachman took the reins, although it surely made them shudder at first and they at first rebelled, but in vain—should not a human being quickly be able to understand what a blessing it is to him that you take the power and give life!

Dear Martha,

Home again, and delighted to find not one but two letters from you in the mail. Dear friend, I never once thought of your Christianity as "stuffy, purely habitual religion," and I hope that even in your darkest closet thoughts you never thought that I was aiming that comment at you! I think that your faith and your relationship to God will always keep you rooted where you should be rooted and will always uproot you from ruts and routines that have become just that and nothing more.

My fear with regard to making sanctification the way of moral perfection is that it will end up in perfectionism. I have seen too many victims of perfectionism to want that to happen to a strong and beautiful doctrine of the Christian Church. I could write a long $1.00 letter to explain myself, but I would rather send you some quotations from The Downward Ascent, a no-longer-available book by a close friend of mine. Indeed, what she says on perfectionism came right out of long conversations the two of us had over coffee and home-baked bread on the subject. You may read her/our comments to your Back-door Neighbors' Bible Study Group if you want to. I wish I could be a mouse hiding under the piano and listen to you all. This is the end of my letter. The rest is quotations.

Love,

Molly

"A saving sense of humor is precisely what perfectionist man and woman trying to create a Utopia of their families do not have. How can they if they feel that they have been saved to make a perfect model of a Christian family? Bernanos describes a perfectionist woman in <u>The Diary of a Country Priest.</u> She was the priest's vestry woman, and her goal 'wasn't to fight dirt but to do away with it altogether, as if that were possible! A parish is bound to be dirty. A whole Christian society's a lot dirtier. She wasn't a real housewife; a real housewife knows her home isn't a shrine. Those are just poet's dreams.'

"Like this vestry-cleaning woman, the perfectionist would sweep God himself out of the family in order to make a clean, respectable place of it. In their zeal for perfection, women have perhaps created more pain, frustration, and suffering in the family than any other member—unless it is the perfectionist father. The suffering of living under a perfectionist father is devastatingly described in Kafka's <u>Letter to His Father.</u>

" 'I was continually in disgrace; either I obeyed your orders, and that was a disgrace, for they applied, after all, only to me; or I was defiant, and that was a disgrace too, for how could I presume to defy you; or I could not obey because I did not, for instance, have your strength, your appetite, your skill, although you expected it of me as a matter of course; this was the greatest disgrace of all.'

"Nathaniel Hawthorne and Herman Melville each wrote a thundering No! to the heresy of human perfectibility. In a story heavy with symbolism, Hawthorne wrote of a young husband who delighted in the flawless beauty of his bride's soul and in her almost flawless physical beauty. However, a tiny birthmark on her face gradually became to him the horrible symbol of the fatal flaw in human nature, a symbol of his wife's susceptibility to sin and death. He resorted to magic and sorcery to remove this flaw and in the process destroyed both his wife and himself.

"Hawthorne suggests that in a desperate attempt to make a flawed and imperfect world perfect, we make it more flawed and imperfect—and sometimes demonically so. In the name of

60

making a more perfect world, perfectionists will kill anybody who gets in their way, will destroy whole populations, all those whose flaws and defects keep their world imperfect.

"Is it Yes to imperfection and No to perfection, then? Yes to impiety, No to piety? Yes to evil-doers, No to do-gooders? Yes to self-indulgence, No to abstinence? Yes to reprobates, No to saints? Yes to sin, No to sanctification? Yes to the oldness of Old Adam, No to the newness in Christ?

"The finger of the Holy Spirit has traced the call to be perfect, to be saints, to newness in Christ, on every page of the New Testament. It is written in blood on the cross. There is no evading that call! But thanks be to God, the communion of saints is not based on human perfectibility but assumes its imperfection and imperfectibility. Our God has chosen to become involved in the divine failure—humanity. Our Savior chose to share with us the pain, punishments, and penalties of being imperfect humans. And God's Secret Agent of Reform chooses to help us imperfect creatures respond to the terrible call to be new creatures in Christ. For it _is_ a terrible call, and it is a long, long painful journey. For there is so much to tear down before the Holy Spirit can build up. There are so many fake props to knock down. And the end of the painful road is not perfection, but perfect humility. Not morbidity and self-loathing, but a humble and contrite heart."

Dear Molly,

Verily, verily, if Princeton University Press were not printing the new translations of Kierkegaard's Works, Emmaus Press would hope to be granted the privilege of doing it. The excerpt you sent me from For Self-Examination corrected—or at least began to correct—my mind-set that the concept of dying-to is the invention of a morbid mentality. Admit it, Molly, neither St. Paul nor St. Søren would be considered these days to have well-adjusted personalities. But they are not, as I at times nastily felt they were, fostering the feeling of being a failure, a flop, a no-body, a zero, a worm. Instead they are fostering the buoyant mentality of those who have been toppled off the throne of self and discover that they have fallen on the other side of death: death to selfish self-seeking, selfish self-interest, selfish ambition, death to the superficial self, death to attachment to trifles. So, Molly, I have worked out a new equation for sanctification:

Detachment from attachment to what is finite = relation to God in and through Christ = through him and in him a new and sanctified relation to everything finite

Does that pass inspection, Madam Supervisor of the Dept. of Sanctification? (Does your function include programming our computers with the fruits of sanctification as well as dealing with the solid waste of sin?)

Whenever you dower me with something from the works of Kierkegaard I trot to my works of Luther. He, too, Molly, speaks of dying twice, "once spiritually unto sin, which is a blessed dying, full of grace and comfort (although to flesh and blood it is painful and bitter) and a lovely, sweet death, for it leads to an entirely heavenly, sure, perfect, and eternal life; and once physical . . . " It seems that St. Martin and St. Søren see pretty much inner-eye to inner-eye.

Ah, St. Molly, it's a blessing to have your letters arriving again after a two-month's dearth that I found to be a kind of death.

Die daily if you will,
but please, never again mail-ly.
(Awful, isn't it?)

Tate

Dear Molly,

You are back again, a letter from you again in the mailbox, and all is right with my world again!

What painful memories the quotations you sent me on perfectionists brought back to me! I feel disloyal writing this, but I grew up in a home my parents were trying to make "a perfect model of a Christian family." They were both like Kafka's father, so my brother and I were always in disgrace. There were two ways open to us when we grew up—either to rebel and be as imperfect as possible or be another perfectionist. My brother chose the former and became, in our parents' eyes, a perfect slob. I chose the latter and became the perfect secretary and housekeeper—and the sour, hypocritical person that I am. Now I watch my sister-in-law trying to make my brother over into her perfect model of a husband. He stays at the office and works overtime rather than go home to her everlasting nagging. I feel so helpless, Molly. Should I speak to her?

Today is Mother's Day. Here is one of my darkest closet-thoughts. Molly, I hate it! I think most of us "maiden ladies" hate it. But today at the evening Baptist service (yes, this regular churchgoer now goes regularly to two church services every Sunday!) the young pastor said that if he had his way Mother's Day would be changed to Mothering Day. Some mothers, he said, do not deserve to be honored. On Mothering Day everyone with mothering love could be honored—be they married or single, blessed with children or childless, male or female—men, he said, can also have mothering love. Animals, birds, and all creatures could also be honored. He recited a long list of people who could be honored—nurses, teachers, doctors, counselors, social workers, clerks, receptionists, secretaries—yes, he said secretaries! Many secretaries, he said, make the place where they work beautiful with mothering love.

That brings me to something I have been bursting to tell you ever since it happened. Mr. Kuhlman took me out to dinner. Dinner, mind you, not lunch! I politely declined a cocktail and chose the cheapest entree on the menu, salisbury steak, which you of course know is simply hamburger with a highfalutin name. Mr. Kuhlman respected my wish not to drink an alcoholic beverage, but he overrode my choice of an entree and ordered roast duck with spiced pears. While we waited for it we drank a sparkling non-alcoholic white grape juice and talked of many things. He told me about his wife and their years together. She must have been wonderful, Molly. We talked about the books Emmaus Press publishes, and I told him which ones I liked and which ones I didn't like. He was really very interested in my opinions. The roast duck was heavenly, and for dessert we had chocolate mousse tarts. I am sure that he had to pay at least $50 for everything! When he brought me home two hours later he thanked me for the evening and then said the strangest thing. He said, "I hope that you can forgive me, Martha." I told him that for the life of me I did not know what for! He just smiled and walked to his car. Molly, what could he have meant?

Love,

Martha

Dear Tate,

Ascension Day

Wingless he rose?
Sans hydrogen
Sans rocket
And against gravity?

Be still, my doubts!
This much I know—

Where once I walked
   world-pressured
   self-cumbered
   sin-dragged
I now walk as the bird walks
that feels its wings.
Divine levity has fluffed and feathered me.

No clod now
No law of gravity—
Grace
Sheer grace!

If He did not ascend—
could I?

Apropos of the dying-to that precedes ascension, ponder these simple statements by better poets than I.

Saint Theresa (1515–1582): "I die because I do not die."

Johann Geørg Hamann (1730–1788): "I had perished had I not perished."

Now ponder these three truths:

1. Dying-to is actually a coming-alive-to, or a being born again.

66

2. No one or nothing can kill someone who has died.
3. In the early Church the martyrs' deaths were celebrated as <u>birth</u>days.

As ever,

Molly

Dear Martha,

Thank you, thank you (or thank your Baptist pastor) for the Mothering Day idea! Of course it's mothering love, not mothers, that ought to be honored. And I thank Christ for redeeming your unhappy past and for making it possible for you to forgive your parents and love them. And for rescuing you from being a "sour, hypocritical person"! He has made those adjectives entirely inappropriate for you, so please do not let me ever catch you using them about yourself again!

So you and your brother were cheated of the Kingdom of the First Spontaneity, the enchanted kingdom of blissful, carefree childhood, the bright and happy Eden of a child before it is invaded by the dragons of evil. So you and your brother were ushered almost at once into the disenchanted country of Ish and never knew the kingdom of Tra-la-la that is every child's right and need to know and experience. But thanks be to God, Martha, you are not cheated of the Kingdom of the Second Spontaneity! I sense this in your letters. You obviously are no longer living in the Country of Ish—all joy spoiled, all pleasure soiled. I'll bet there isn't even a line-crack in your being from your unhappy childhood! Cheated of the joy of the first immediacy, you are born by the grace of God into the second immediacy.

You were not hugged by your parents, but you now know yourself hugged by God, and you are hugging him back! How do I know? Because you hug me! In every letter you hug me! And I am quite sure that you are hugging all the people you are with every day, because that is what people do who know themselves hugged by God.

I am sure that is why Mr. Kuhlman said, "Martha, forgive me!" Men are often very blind and do not see things that are as plain as a barn door. He saw you every day but was blind to your

warm and wonderful and hugging self. Apparently his eyes
were opened that evening you had dinner together, and when
he said goodbye to you at 601 Oak Street he was asking your
forgiveness for having been so blind, for not seeing the *real* you
all those years. He asked to be forgiven for being so sapheaded.

Love,

Molly

Dear Molly,

So you are a poet, too. You do indeed write as if you feel wings.
But you did not say anything about physical levitation. St. Catherine of Geneva is said frequently to have been raised from the
floor while receiving communion. Indeed, this seems to have
been a phenomenon rather commonly experienced by saints.
(You see, Molly, you have gotten me into hagiology. Isn't that a
horrible word for a study of the lives and legends of the saints?)
What about the stigmata? St. Francis is reported to have received the wounds of the crucified Christ on his body, and when
St. Catherine of Siena, a Dominican, later experienced the same
miracle, the Franciscans were incensed and claimed the exclu-
sive right to a saint with the stigmata. It became quite an unholy ecclesiastical battle. What do you say to all that, Molly
Mortensen? Imagination? Hysteria? Did Catherine of Siena
show the wounds on her body to any Church council, or did they
have to take her word for it?

We celebrated Pentecost in a very holy-spirited way in our
church today. The miracle of Pentecost is easier for me to ac-
cept than the levitation and stigmatas of the saints. It had too
many witnesses to dispute that it happened! It is my favorite
holy day. Christmas has become more and more the celebration
of the Son of God becoming sweet little baby Jesus and less and
less the celebration of the Son of God taking upon himself our
human nature. Because we were childless, Christmas had its
elements of sadness for my wife and me. Easter is rapidly being
taken over by our secular society and turned into a pagan celebration of fertility. So far, thank God, "they" have not been
able to get their profaning fingers on Pentecost. I am sure that
someone somewhere is trying to develop a plant with flowers

the shape of tongues of fire that will become as identified with Pentecost as the Easter lily is with Easter and the poinsettia with Christmas.

The Holy Spirit certainly must be the Chief Engineer in the Dept. of Sanctification. If he did not act upon the human mind and will, how could mind and will become means of sanctification, as I firmly believe they are. I know it isn't popular to mention hell these days, but there are low ways to hell as well as highways to heaven. Unsanctified minds and wills can and often do pervert the personality and reroute persons onto the speedway to hell.

Do I sound the very opposite of Pentecost, Molly? Almost hypochondriacal? Not really! I prayed with the spirit this morning. I sang with the spirit. But, like Paul, I insist on praying and singing with my mind and will as well. Is that why I truly do love this holy day? It assures me that the Holy Spirit will supervise my mind, will and heart. I'm not forgetting the heart, Molly. I truly believe that he will quicken them with his power when my natural powers fail or take an unsanctified direction.

In the fellowship of the Holy Spirit,
Tate

P.S. Ponder this: By the severest standards we are all hypocrites.

May 23

Dear Molly,

I planned to write to you last night after I came home from the evening service at the Baptist church. It was more exciting than ever. They sang and prayed as if they were possessed with the Spirit as on that first Pentecost day. But I found the pastor's short sermon even more exciting. He spoke more plainly and directly about the Holy Spirit than any preacher I have ever heard. Lutheran preachers hardly ever talk about the Holy Spirit! I was going to try to tell you what he said, but I decided to ask the pastor for a copy of his sermon to send to you. Well, he was very kind and made two copies, one for you and one for me. His topic was "Come, Holy Spirit, into our dailyness," and he seemed to be speaking to me alone. In a way it was a sobering sermon for some of my new Baptist friends. I think he was trying to steer them away from what he called "fuzzy thinking" about the Holy Spirit. But he spoke very directly to my guilt of "confusing spiritual stagnation with the peace that passes all understanding." When you write, please tell me if you think his sermon is as wonderful as I think it is.

Love,

Martha

Come, Holy Spirit, into Our Dailyness
A sermon delivered at the evening service in Grace Baptist Church, Rocky Point, Massachusetts, on Pentecost Sunday, by Justin T. Brown

Have I come to sling slogans? The kind of slogans bad theology likes to invent? —Bad theology, my friends, may well be far worse than bad morals!

Slogans like these:

Is your daily life stale and rancid with sameness? Try the Holy Spirit!

Are you frustrated and despondent? Is your daily life meaningless and empty? Try the Holy Spirit!

Is your daily life a mere existing? Do you feel like a cabbage, a turnip, a rutabaga? Do you want to come alive, feel power, strength, joy? Try the Holy Spirit!

Is your mind like a dustmop collecting all the dust and lint in daily existence, absorbed in everything that makes life dirty, gray, and lusterless? Why not try the Holy Spirit!

No, I have not come to sling slogans. If your dailyness is a staleness, I think I would rather tell you to go jogging every day, change your hairdo, anything, anything but ask you to insult, abuse, misuse, and grieve the Holy Spirit.

All this whining and whimpering we human beings do in the name of the Holy Spirit! I'm bored, Lord. Send your Holy Spirit. Make my life interesting, exciting! I'm a failure, Lord. Make me a success. I'm depressed, Lord. Make me cheerful. I'm frustrated, Lord. Make things go my way, make my wife, my husband, my mother-in-law, my children, my friends, MAKE EVERYBODY do what I want them to do the way I want them to do it and when I want them to do it.

It is not, it never was, and it never will be the holy will of the Holy Spirit that your will and my will be done on this earth. It is not, it never was, and it never will be the holy concern of the Holy Spirit that you and I live lives that are interesting, glowing, and exciting. Lives free from tensions, problems, unsolvable problems. The holy concern of the Holy Spirit is that the will of God and of his Son Christ Jesus be done on earth as it is in heaven—through you and through me. Then and then only is he truly worshiped.

This practically eliminates the Holy Spirit as God's chief psychiatrist and psychologist, which much of the fuzzy thinking in religion makes the Holy Spirit out to be and tempts us to use him for our self-centered, selfish purposes when it is exactly the opposite—he wants to use you and me for God's holy purposes.

"But," you say, "Christ himself said, 'I will send you a Counselor, a Comforter.'" And truly he did. Did he ever! We are celebrating that great sending today. The trouble is that our fuzzy thinking has confused divine counseling with marriage counseling, career counseling, practical advice, tranquilizing pills, the psychiatrist's couch, and all that. The world's counselors are interested in our well-being, our well-feeling, and that is all right as far as it goes—but how far does it go? It rarely gets beyond self-centeredness, a primary concern with me, my self-fulfillment, my self-identity, my will, me, me, my, my—. The world's counselors advise us not to set our ideals so high that they are unrealistic, impractical, impossible. This, they say, is the source of our discontent and despair. Be sensible, they say, Be realistic. Avoid impossibilities. Lower your sights.

And what does the heavenly Counselor say? "I have not come to comfort you by reducing Christ's demands. I have come to give you power to do all the impossible things God and Christ have commanded you to do. Go, therefore, and love as Christ loved, forgive as Christ forgave, worship the Lord your God as Christ commanded you to worship the Lord your God, in deed and in truth, in your daily lives."

The last thing the Holy Spirit wants in you and me is a mind that confuses spiritual stagnation with the peace that passes all understanding. He is out to shatter that peace of mind. It is the worst possible kind of mind and spirit for him to work in. Indeed, I am sure that the Holy Spirit finds no one quite so "ungetatable" as good brought-up Christians whose good has gone wrong and they do not know it. I am sure that when he makes his weekly report he shakes his head and says, "I've tried everything! Stung their souls with gadflies, scattered thorns in them—they simply tidy up their souls and make everything cozy and comfortable again. Far from being haunted by the truth of themselves and of the cross, they bask in their virtues, idolize the cross, and loll in its shadow." The twice-borners give him trouble, too. When he makes his weekly report on them, he no doubt sighs and says, "There's no converting the converted. They stop at two, think that's enough, and don't seem to realize that a conversion is obsolete every day and that one can never be reborn often enough."

Come, Holy Spirit, into our dailyness! If he really does come, do you realize what may happen? To you and to me? He may puncture, pierce, deflate our self-importance, self-esteem, self-satisfaction, self-sufficiency. And that, my friends, is excruciatingly painful! But he has to do this to make a new creation, reconstructed upon Christ and not upon yourself or myself. He has to do it to create a new heart and a new spirit.

Come, Holy Spirit, into our dailyness! Do you know what else might happen if he really does come? He will give us X-ray eyes that see into the mysterious drama of souls, souls other than our own, the sufferings of others, sufferings other than our own sufferings. We will literally live among naked people in a naked world. Our eyes will see what they never saw before. They will penetrate loneliness, misery, wretchedness, despair behind all their masks.

So, instead of delivering us from suffering and evil, the Holy Spirit delivers us into suffering and evil. He says, "Open your eyes. There it is, right under your nose; it was there all the time, even within your own four walls. Put yourself at its disposal. Make yourself available. Do this, and you will be doing the will of God and of his Son Jesus Christ."

Let us pray:

Come, Holy Spirit, into our dailyness. Refuse to lose track of us, pursue us in all our masks and masquerades. Come, God's

75

Hound Dog, track us down in all our flights, escapes, and evasions. Come, Holy Provoker, push us, pull us, prompt us, tease us, please us, displease us. Come, Holy Tenacity, refuse to let go of us. If we shut the door in your face, go to the back door. If we slam the back door, come in through the cracks. Come, Holy Oddity, whimsical as the wind, surprise us at our most unexpecting moments as you surprised many a God-resister and brought him or her to faith in your Son Christ Jesus, as you surprised Saul on his way to Damascus to capture and kill Christians and turned him into Paul, the greatest missionary the world has known. Unplug us when we fill up with self-pity and misery. Rescue us when we drown in our dailyness. Restore in us the joy of our salvation in Jesus Christ. Pour your love and joy and power into us today as you poured it into the thousands on Pentecost Day. Come into our dailyness, O Holy Spirit, be our divine income, our holy, incorruptible income—and then, O Holy Spirit, help us to spend that income, spend it like the rich-in-spirit men and women you have made us to be! Amen.

June 15

Dear Fisherman Tate,

It's three weeks since I received your Molly-baiting letter. I must say you dangle some rather luring questions on your hook, but before rising to your bait I must tell you that I have been in Madison, Wisconsin, for a month. My daughter Linda gave birth to her second child and first daughter on June 1, and her husband, Jim, urgently wanted me to come a week in advance of the due-date. A year ago they had a stillborn baby, and I think Jim wanted me to be there as a cushion for all three of them in case they experienced that sadness again. Beg to report that Laura is a healthy, happy, beautiful girl, and brother Sam age three is ecstatic.

But Linda and Jim's sad loss a year ago helps me answer your question about saints and stigmatas. I am sure that in some instances there was fakery, especially if the supposed saint had no invisible sanctity to match his or her outward and visible sanctity. But I am also sure that the true saints felt the wounds of Christ. You know, of course, that people who have had a limb amputated feel very real pain in the limb that is not there. St. Catherine of Siena felt the suffering of Christ so profoundly that she could very well have felt the wounds on her own body. I assure you that when Linda's second baby was stillborn, I, her mother, felt my daughter's grief and pain in my own breast!

As for the Holy Spirit's role in the mind and will, will is at home in the mind, isn't it? Intelligence, too? And understanding? But intellect, the IQ, and understanding do not play a major role in the process of sanctification, as is clearly apparent in the discrepancy between our understanding and our action. (Yes, indeed, by the severest standard of judgment we are all hypocrites!) Moreover, anyone who is at all involved in spiritual ministry with people who are mentally handicapped (I teach

77

a class of mentally handicapped persons in our church) soon becomes convinced that geniuses fare far worse than the mentally retarded when it comes to faith. The IQ, it seems to me, is what Scripture calls a worthless servant in the process of sanctification. But the LQ, the Love Quotient, that is another matter! The trouble is that we know enough! What we need to do is to exercise God's glorious gift of free will, the gift of choice. So I agree wholeheartedly with you that the Holy Spirit's role in our human wills is by no means second-string!

I have not quoted Kierkegaard for some time, so here he is on the will (slightly revised to accommodate us women!): "A Christian in the process of sanctification is a woman of will, a man of will, who no longer wills her or his will, but with the passion of a radically changed will wills God's will."

But it takes a woman to say it in down-to-earth language! Hear my favorite poet, Emily Dickinson:

> A deed knocks first at thought
> And then—it knocks at will.
> There is the manufacturing spot
> And will at home and well.
>
> It then goes out an act
> Or is entombed so still
> That only to the ear of God
> Its doom is audible.

Now, Sir, do you have a Martin Luther quotation to match these two?

As ever,

Molly

78

June 15

Dear Martha,

Please thank your Baptist pastor for his sermon on the Holy
Spirit. I'll bet the saints above applauded so loudly when they
cavesdropped and heard it that the angels had to cover their
ears with their wings. Thank you for sending me a copy.

I have been slow about answering because I have been a full-
time grandmother in Madison, Wisconsin, this past month.
Grandchild number 11 arrived June 1, a beautiful baby girl who
was baptized last Sunday and given the name of Laura. Linda,
my daughter, and Jim, her husband, wanted me to stand with
them and three-year-old Sam as a family at the baptismal font.
Laura wore the dress Linda wore when she was baptized, the
very same dress that I, Laura's grandmother, wore when I was
baptized! But I was not thinking of that or of whether the pot
roast would be done for the christening dinner when we got
home. In fact, I honestly and truly believe that the Holy Spirit
used the blessed occasion of the baptism to infiltrate my mind
with an exciting thought about—guess what—sanctification!

As I watched that tiny baby signed and sealed on the forehead
with the Cross and heard the pastor say, "Receive the sign of
the holy Cross in token that henceforth you shall know the
Lord, and the power of his Resurrection, and the fellowship of
his suffering," I had the sudden thought that Laura, but twelve
days old, was now a saint, a genuine unqualified saint. From
now on she would stand "in the power of his resurrection" and
"in the fellowship of his suffering." In no other religion could
something so radical and audacious be said, but in the crazy up
side-down paradoxical Christian faith with its Gospel of the
new creation in Jesus Christ it is theologically sound and correct to say that Laura, but 12 days old, is a sanctified saint.

All the rest of that christening day I pondered that thought

79

every chance I had. Little twelve-day old Laura is not on the way _toward_ sanctification. She is not beginning a lifetime climbing a ladder _up to_ sanctification and sainthood. I laughed out loud once and startled Sam, whom I was rocking to sleep because he was so excited by everything happening that he could not fall asleep. The preposterous thought hit me that in regard to sanctification the prepositions toward, up, up to, and the concept of climbing are un-Christian, at least un-Lutheran. And the song "We are climbing Jacob's Ladder" is actually heretical! Laura is already there—_in_ sanctification, safely and securely in relationship to the holy, immortal God! She is now on the way to becoming what she already is—a saint.

So, Martha, that was the gift of the Holy Spirit to me, personally, last Sunday—the amazing thought that sanctification is a relationship to God _in_ which we rest as securely as a child rests in a loving relationship to loving parents.

Laura is a saint, and so are you, Martha, and so am I—

Namely,
Molly

80

Dear Molly,

Congratulations on the new grandchild. Lucky grandmother!
Lucky grandchild! Does that make eleven?

I really ought not write to you on Sir Thomas More's Day
because, as you probably know, he opposed Luther. However, I
admire the man because he performed what I consider the true
function of a saint (and a saintly Christian): to be a finger that
points the way—and at the same time be a sign of contradiction.
We don't all have to lose our heads, as did Sir Thomas, but like
him and the true saints, we should be willing to struggle for
what seems to be right and just and be willing to risk the consequences, come what may.

When you wrote that sassy letter to Emmaus Press last January, did you foresee the consequences? Do you realize that it is
your fault and yours alone that I am sifting through hagiogra-
phical literature and trying to distinguish between the "saint as
thaumaturge and the saint as paradigmatic model"? Do you
blanch to see me using those words? Your fault, my dear. Yours
entirely.

So you are expecting a "matching Luther quotation" from
me. Listen, Woman, we are not engaged in a game of one-up-
manship (or one-upwomanship, if you will). Nevertheless, here
is one without equal.

May God in His mercy save me from a Christian Church
where there are none but saints. I want to be with that little
company and in the Church where there are faint-hearted
and weak people, the sick, and those who are aware of their
sin, misery, and wretchedness, and feel it, and who cry to
God without ceasing and sigh unto Him for comfort and help

and believe in the forgiveness of sins and suffer persecution for the Word's sake. Satan is a cunning rogue. Through his fanatics he seeks to make the simple-minded believe that the preaching of the Gospel is useless. The right approach is quite different. It consists of such things as walking in holy ways, taking our cross upon us and suffering much persecution. Through such false appearances of self-chosen sanctity (which is contrary to the Word of God) many are led astray. Yet our sanctification and justification is Christ in whom (and not in ourselves) we are perfect, and therein I find my comfort and strength in St. Paul's word, that "Christ Jesus is of God made unto us wisdom and righteousness, and sanctification and redemption."

Someone may say, and many, indeed, have said it: Is there nothing to do, then? Both Luther and Kierkegaard say: Nothing at all, nothing to do but by the grace of God to become what we already are by the grace of God. And do we not both agree, Molly, that we are not even required to become that, become what we already are—saints, but, because we are accepted into relationship to the holy immortal God as we are, we do not remain as we were.

Grace and peace!

Tate

Dear Molly,

Congratulations on your new granddaughter. Laura is a lovely name, as were your thoughts while she was being signed with the Cross. I like the idea of sanctification as "by the grace of God becoming what we already are by the grace of God," but I find it hard to get away from the idea that was drilled into me—that it is struggling and working to make myself holy, pure, and perfect. For me sanctification only served to make me feel guilty because I never was able to measure up. But when I accepted the standards of moral perfection set by the Christians I knew I found that I could measure up pretty well. I didn't fornicate, I didn't drink or dance or swear or play cards. I began to feel pretty good about myself and to think of myself as good, decent, conscientious, hardworking Martha. But the secret Mary deep down inside me whispered that there was more to sanctification than that. And then you came along, Molly! My Church Press rejected your manuscript on sanctification, and somehow I find myself writing to you and telling you my secret thoughts! Here are some more of them!

Our Back-door Neighbors' Bible Study has met. It was humbling and embarrassing for me and Sally (my Baptist friend who lives in the building) to knock on every apartment door and invite people to come. One man slammed the door in our faces, but four women came to our first meeting and six to our next one. One of the women is a born-again Christian, and she is the one who really gives us trouble. She thinks the Holy Spirit tells her when to water the geraniums, when to buy another bottle of vanilla, what dress to wear to church, etc. Molly, she makes the Holy Spirit a divine babysitter who never lets us little infant spirits out of his sight. Please tell me that my dismay (bordering on disgust) is theologically sound!

83

As for my sister-in-law, she is certainly not a born-again Christian. She is a "good" born-and-brought-up Christian. Molly, she is making my brother's life a hell on earth! I invited her to our Bible Study in the hope we could somehow openly discuss and confess our sins and the Holy Spirit could then get at her through the Word, but she promptly informed me that she has her own Bible Study group plus a Prayer Group. I'll bet she prays with her prayer partners that my brother will stop smoking cigars (which I am sure he does so that he can have at least one pitiful little self-indulgence in his wretched life).

Oh, Molly, Molly! You have convinced me that I am sanctified, but I am still sinfully critical and judgmental!

Love,

Martha

Dear Tate,

This is a short quick note to tell you that I am about to vanish for two months and leave no trace behind and no forwarding address. For thirty-five years our family (beginning, as all families do, with two) has done this disappearing act and buried itself in the forest in northern Minnesota. (My husband literally is buried up there, and so also will I be.) The children are continuing the tradition of slipping away from their otherwise life and of getting lost as long as their vacations permit. During that time we do not write letters, even to dear friends to whom writing letters is sheer unadulterated fun—

such as is writing to you!

Molly

July 1

Dear Martha,

No, you are not critical and judgmental! Being sanctified does not mean abandoning value judgments!

This note is short and to the point. I am about to vanish for two months and leave no trace behind and no forwarding address. Where? Where we have disappeared for two months every summer for 35 years—into the wilderness in northern Minnesota. My children continue the tradition and prefer to come up there in their too-short vacations. During that time we do not write letters, even to dear souls such as you, Martha!

Until September 1!

Molly

P.S. But up there in the woods I shall pray that God's Secret Agent of Reform will find a crack in the souls of your born-again neighbor and unborn-again sister-in-law and squeeze in and begin to work a change. Remember what he did to that ruthless, cold-blooded iceberg Saul of Tarsus!

September 1

Dear Martha,

Home again—to electric lights, running water, indoor plumbing, refrigerator, flower boxes ablaze with fall colors—all of which I do not miss up there but do appreciate down here.

How is the Back-door Neighbors' Bible Study going? Has God's Secret Agent of Reform made any progress with your sister-in-law? Are you still going regularly to two church services every Sunday? Is the Baptist pastor still preaching mighty, relevant sermons? How is your boss at Emmaus Press? Still rejecting manuscripts? Has the Press published anything lately that you think I ought to read? Is your secret Mary-self thinking thoughts your Martha-self can't quite stomach? Your Molly-friend can, because she has an unshockable, ironclad stomach!

You don't have to answer all my questions, Martha! I'm not pumping you for answers as much as I am priming your pump to get you started. Did you ever have to do that with your outdoor pump?

Thirsting for a letter from you!

Molly

Dear Tate,

Like it or not, ready or not, here I am again—mellowed with sun, amber river water, and love (God's unfailing, children's tenderly tolerant, grandchildren's and granddogs' unconditional), and eager to resume our correspondence. Where were we? Do I recollect correctly that we were discussing sanctification (prompted by Emmaus Press's rejection of my manuscript on that subject)? How many manuscripts have you rejected this year? Have you published any good ones recently? What do I mean by "good"? Books that pierce the native egoism and ebullient self-sufficiency of me, Molly Mortensen, and show me that I—not my mother, not my father, not my children, but ME, oh Lord—need God. Otherwise how can the Holy Spirit commence any change in the hidden depths of my innermost heart? How can I ever begin to "bear fruit unto holiness"?

As ever,

Molly

P.S. Did you know that Kierkegaard wrote a discourse he entitled, "To Need God Is the Highest Human Perfection and to Need God Is Perfection Itself"?

Dear Molly,

Your letter was in my mailbox on Wildwood Lane when I returned from a trying day at Emmaus Press. It is not easy to dash the hopes of hopeful authors and to reject their manuscripts (unless what they write is utterly hopeless.) So put out was I by your vanishing act this summer that I was resolved not to answer you for two months after the arrival of your first post-disappearance letter (an eye for an eye, tit for tat: Tate would be tacit), but the minute I saw your letter I realized that I would only be punishing myself, not you. So with unseemly haste I am responding at once. Hans, my black labrador, is begging to be taken for a run (I bike and he runs alongside), but he will have to wait until I finish this letter. We can bike/run to Rocky Point and catch the six o'clock mail truck pickup.

We have not published anything in the last year—or ever, for that matter—that is making the ten-bestseller list, but we have published some books that I am proud to have a maieutic part in bringing into existence. I am sending you a package of them.

Do you realize, Molly, that you have consciously or unconsciously made a shift in your concerns about the subject of sanctification? One could whimsically call it an about-face. Before your disappearing act you wrote about sanctification, about the call to be holy, about becoming what we already are. Now you express a longing to see the fruits of holiness hanging from the branches of the tree that is your own individual Molly-self. Ah, Molly, I went through that painful self-scrutiny and about-face myself before I came to Emmaus Press. For several years I taught Christian ethics at a small Protestant college in New York. Finally I became sick of talking about the obligation to act according to God's Word and will, sick of talking about the danger of talking about the obligation to act according to God's

Word and will, sick of talking about the danger of talking about the obligation to act according to God's Word and will. I decided to act. I resigned from teaching Christian ethics and together with some pastors started an ecumenical advocacy program that brought church members face to face with the suffering right under their noses. Why did I quit after only two years and move to Emmaus Press and this small Massachusetts town? Mostly because of my wife Rachel's illness. Here I could better give her the increasing care she needed. Then, too, I believed that books make a difference, and that an editor can make a difference in the quality of the books a press publishes. I still believe that.

I didn't mean to become autobiographical. I only want to tell you that I know personally that about-faces are painful.

But Molly, dear Molly, the Holy Spirit, whose main job is to make you and me what we already are in Christ, is not itching to turn our gaze in self-loathing and anxiety upon ourselves and our imperfections or the problems caused by our imperfections. His primary work is to direct us to Christ—not primarily to his teaching (for us to teach about, write about, talk about), but to his person. Christ the teacher is more important than his teaching.

Hans is tugging at the cuff of my pants!

> As ever—
> No, more than ever,
>
> Tate

Dear Molly,

Praise God, as my new Baptist friends say, you are back! Your letter came yesterday, but our Bible Study lasted so long last night that I had to get my sleep if I was going to be Mr. Kuhlman's pluperfect secretary—that is what he called me last week when I came back from my vacation. He said my substitute convinced him that I am not just perfect, I am a pluperfect secretary.

So many questions in your letter! Yes, I still go regularly to two church services. Last Sunday morning Pastor Oliver (the Lutheran pastor) talked on aims that go wrong. It was so good I took notes on the service folder. He said that the health fanatic's aim can go wrong in the pursuit of physical perfection for the sake of physical perfection. (Are they mad about jogging and marathons in Minnesota, too?) The intellectual's aim can go wrong in the pursuit of intellectual superiority for the sake of intellectual superiority (wanting to be the most brilliant scientist, the most published scholar, the most distinguished or popular professor). The spiritual fanatic's aim can go wrong in the pursuit of spiritual experience and spiritual perfection for the sake of spiritual experience and spiritual perfection (wanting to be more unworldly and more spiritual than worldly and unspiritual people).

Like my sister-in-law, Molly! She is coming to our Back-door Neighbors' Bible Study, but I am sure it is just because she wants to show the rest of us how unworldly and spiritual she is—and how much more she knows about the Bible and theology than we do! And how she can pray longer. And Molly, she did! She prayed that my brother would stop smoking. You probably think I am being catty. Well, maybe I am! But I know for sure that I'm sorry I invited her to come to Bible Study! All she does is argue! Right now we are having an argument about whether love is a fruit of the Spirit or a gift of the Spirit. She says it is a fruit, and the rest of us say it is a gift. She will not budge an inch. Can you help us out, Molly? We meet every two weeks, so could you please answer by that time?

Love,

Martha

P.S. I think these are Martha-thoughts, not Mary-thoughts! Maybe I am insulting Martha to say that!

Humanum enim est piccare, diabolicum vero perseverare.

Dear Tate,

No, I am not trying to impress you, Tate. I am merely impressed by this ancient Father of the Church, who tells me that to fall into sin is human, to remain in sin is devilish. The first shows us to be a weak people. The second makes us like the devil, who to this day is of the same mind as he was at his first fall. You must dearly love St. John Chrysostom, because he was a master of excellent homilies, thundered against pomp and luxury, denounced ignorance of Scripture as the source of all heresy, and did not talktalktalk <u>about</u> the Christian faith but acted upon it, even when he knew that he would die for it.

Yes, I <u>am</u> becoming personal about sanctification. In many ways I am a patient person, but in others I am quite impatient. Impatient to see happen what ought to happen. I suppose that is why I am forever being made chairperson of things—rummage sales, church bazaars and suppers, fund drives. Now I am impatient to see something happen to, in, with ME. No, I have not formed a self-improvement committee and appointed myself chairwoman. I am humbly aware that my sanctification is not my doing. Jesus Christ accomplished it. His Holy Spirit must perfect it in me, must gradually form in me a sanctified disposition of thought and action. So my prayer these days is: O Holy Spirit, perfect in me the work begun by Jesus Christ.

But as I become more personal about sanctification, I am also becoming more troubled by the Church, the Protestant Church. Why is my local church life so dull and mediocre and uninspir-

93

ing? Why do I so seldom feel the mystery and power of the faith there? Why don't I experience "little Pentecosts" in the pew? Am I right in feeling that the Protestant Church is not very helpful in expectantly inviting the sanctified disposition of thought and action in its members? Why is Catholic spirituality a better "manufacturing" place for saints than Protestant spirituality? The people in my lifetime in whom the Holy Spirit has perfected the work begun by Christ, and who in my opinion qualify to be canonized, are Dorothy Day, Jean Vanier, and Mother Theresa—and all three are Catholics!

And what about suffering, Tate? Why is the Protestant Church so silent about it? Isn't suffering also a gift to help us make progress in the process of becoming what Christ has already made us? Aren't trials and suffering a part of "bringing us up"? Did not the author of the letter to the Hebrews write, "Suffering is part of your <u>training</u>." The emphasis is his, not mine! Are not all the trials of life a part of bringing us up? Why, then, did they change that petition in the Lord's Prayer to "Save us from the time of trial"?

Kierkegaard has a lot to say about suffering. At times he seems to declare that if one has not suffered for the faith, then one for certain is not a Christian. If he is right, then I for certain am not a Christian, for I cannot recall ever having suffered for my faith! I've suffered the universally human sufferings, of course. The anguish of my husband's death twenty years ago in a head-on collision with a drunk driver. Watching the children struggle through the consequences of some of their wrong choices. But faith-suffering? No, never!

What do you have to say to this perplexed but not really suffering woman? What does Luther say?

Yours,

Molly

P.S. If I were 50, my friends would blame "change of life" for this present spiritual quandary. But I am 60, long past the "change of life," and I want my life <u>changed.</u>

September 15

Dear Martha,

What good letters you write! I'm glad your Lutheran pastor preaches as "good" as your Baptist pastor. When you see him next, slyly slip him a name for the religion practiced by fanatic joggers, pushuppers, and special diet fiends: Methuselahism, the religion of living as long as one can. Physically, that is. No concern therein about living for eternity!

So the Back-door Neighbors' Bible Study Group is already embroiled in a theological squabble! That's what happens when we human beings with our half-truths begin to argue as if they were whole truths and nothing but the truth. Only Christ can be that for us! I am unordained and have no theological training whatever. All I know is Luther's Catechism, his small Catechism. All I know is that I "cannot by my own understanding or effort believe in Jesus Christ my Lord or come to Him, but the Holy Spirit called me through the Gospel, enlightened me with his gifts, and sanctified and kept me in true faith." But maybe that is sufficient to help you and me to settle this theological squabble together.

"Enlightened me with his gifts." Surely love is the Holy Spirit's greatest gift. But it is also a fruit! Sometimes it is difficult to differentiate between gifts of the Spirit and fruits of the Spirit, but it seems to me that when it comes to love there is no problem. Love is both gift and fruit. Love poured in is the gift. Love poured out is the fruit. Love is the income, the incoming of the Holy Spirit. Love is the outgoing, the spending of the love income—freely, fearlessly. You and I are love millionaires, Martha. Love millionaires do not hoard the gift of love like misers but give it as freely as it is given. Love is the import. Love is the export. Love is sanctification. Love is striving to become what one already is—sanctified. Love is grace. Love is works of love.

96

There is no such thing as a loveless, workless faith. We Lutherans have misused Luther on that score. He never said, "Away with works!" He said, "Away with works-righteousness!"

Here is a joke you can tell your Bible Study Group. I heard it from a Lutheran pastor with a robust Lutheran sense of humor. A Jewish rabbi, a Catholic priest, and a Lutheran pastor showed up at the gates of hell. "Why are you here?" the astounded gatekeeper asked the rabbi. "I committed a blasphemy against the Holy Name." "And why are you here?" the demon asked the priest. "I committed a sexual sin." "And why are you here?" the demon asked the Lutheran pastor. "I committed a good work."

As for your sister-in-law, Martha, may I say that you seem to have a mother-relation to your brother. Nothing wrong in that, unless you harbor what seems to be natural mothers' feelings about their sons (both my mother and my mother-in-law had them!): No woman is good enough for my son! Is there a little bit of that in your antipathy to your brother's wife?

I have not made a practice of hurling Bible verses at you in my letters, but here comes one. Catch it! Read it! Ponder it! 1 Peter 3:13–17.

In his love—both gift and fruit,

Molly

Dear Molly,

"Where does Molly find all her saints?" I asked myself. "Of course! She has a Catholic calendar!" So I got myself a calendar from my priest friend, and now I can keep up with you, Saint Molly! Today is the Feast Day of the French priest who founded the Society of Lazarites, dedicated to "the religious instruction of the lower classes, the training of the clergy, the relief or redemption of prisoners in Barbary [where Paul was a slave to the Barbary pirates for several years] and foreign missions." Another saint who <u>acted,</u> who used the gifts of God to bear fruit for him, which seems to be a primary qualification of a saint, doesn't it? And another saint who suffered. Ah, Molly, don't tell me you have not suffered! At least somewhere and sometime between the two poles, "Ouch! I hurt" and "My God, my God, why have you forsaken me?"

Is it not true, I wonder, that we do not experience much suffering for our faith these days because we are what someone, I don't know who, called nibblers of the possible instead of snatchers after the impossible. Christ asks the impossible of us. Were we to act upon it, we would indeed suffer! The Church asks the possible, and we church members manage by nibbling to meet our local budgets and send some money to missions and charity. I wonder if we do not experience much suffering because we symbolize the Holy Spirit as a gentle, hovering white dove. The things that keep us from growing in grace and holiness need a hawk, a vulture, an eagle to tear them from our innards. And that is no fun! I can hear the Holy Spirit saying, "I have not come to comfort you by reducing Christ's demands. I have come to give you power to do all the things God and Christ have commanded you to do: Go ye therefore. Be perfect.

98

Love as I have loved. Forgive as I have forgiven."

You ask if Luther has something to say on suffering. He does indeed, and it's so tough it sounds as if it came from Kierkegaard's pen, or Paul's. He says "we must receive all suffering as a holy thing, for it truly is a holy thing." But he warns against imposing upon ourselves a cross or suffering of our own choosing.

> ... precisely those who teach so much about a cross and suffering and praise it so highly know least of Christ and His cross, because they claim their own suffering to be meritorious. My friend, such is not the meaning. Neither is any man constrained or forced to it. If you will not suffer without thought of merit, then leave suffering alone and at the same time deny Christ. This you surely know, that if you will not suffer, you cannot be a servant of Christ. So you may choose which you like of the two: whether you suffer or you deny Christ.

To which I say, "Ach du lieber!" I can hear you say, "Oof!"
Have you read Saul Bellow's Henderson the Rain King? If so, did you come across the line "Suffering is about the only reliable burster of the spirit's sleep"?

More than ever,

Tate

September 28

Molly, dear Molly—

I had that spanking coming! I mean what you said about my probably having that mother/daughter-in-law complex. I confess that I do feel very motherly toward my brother and that no woman is good enough for him. Thank you for the spanking, and please do it again if I deserve it. I must say that you even spank lovingly and kindly.

We had our Back-door Neighbors' Bible Study last night. Eight women now come. I think they like the fact that we do not have one leader who conducts (or controls??) everything. My sister-in-law tried to make herself that the time before last, but she was put in her place ("with courtesy and respect and with a clear conscience"—1 Peter 3:16, Molly, dear!). They seem to like the free and open discussion (no closed closets!).

We quickly agreed with you that love is both a gift of the Spirit and a fruit of the Spirit. But just to show you that we can also think for ourselves, we discussed something you did not even touch on—loving what is ugly. Without the gift of the Holy Spirit's love, how could we ever bear <u>that</u> fruit? We are quite able to love our good and friendly neighbors, but we could not love our mean, unfriendly, or indifferent neighbors, to say nothing of our enemies. My sister-in-law (I felt myself loving her for it, Molly!) came up with the thought that it is easy to love children when they are obedient and respectful, but when they are scornful of their parents and do every hurtful thing to show it, then it is tough to love them. You see, my sister-in-law and brother are having a tough time with their teenage children right now.

Someone else had read C. S. Lewis's <u>The Screwtape Letters</u> and said that the Holy Spirit also keeps us from being vain about our love-fruits. She said, "We can be sure that His Satanic Un-

100

holiness says to the demon underlings he assigned to the followers of his Holy Enemy, 'If you can get your charges to be con-
scious of their sanctity our battle is won.' " Someone else told us
that once she had praised someone in her church who had taken
a family whose house had burned into her home, and the woman
had calmly answered, "Yes, I know, the devil has already told
me how wonderful I am."

So you see, Molly, it was a great meeting! But then (my closet
door is open!), then over coffee and caramel bars we started to
talk about why young people do not go to church. And then,
Molly, every mean and criticizing thing we could say about
them came out! I tried to steer us onto a positive road, remem-
bering some things you have written to me, but my sister-in-law
took us down the negative road. What started out as a beautiful
Bible study about loving as a gift and a fruit ended as an ugly
demonstration of the bitter fruit of unlove! Pray for us, Molly.

Love,

Martha

P.S.[1] I cried for an hour when I went to bed.

P.S.[2] Why don't most young people go to church, Molly?

Dear Tate,

St. Francis—everybody's favorite saint! What Catholic, Protestant, or Orthodox has not been stirred by this humble man's imitation of Christ! Who, if he or she has encountered St. Francis in any way, has not perceived the way of sanctity as an exciting and extraordinary adventure—and at least for a brief moment longed to walk that road. For a brief moment, before we once again believed with the world that wealth and property are more satisfying and exciting than poverty and unchastity more desirable and pleasurable than chastity.

I have been wondering where you got all your Luther quotations, wondered if you were a walking encyclopedia on Luther—if so, what was this laywoman doing corresponding with you? This week I stumbled on your secret! You are exposed, Sir! I went to a Hospital Auxiliary Book Sale and found an anthology of Luther quotations entitled Day by Day We Magnify Thee. It's a great book for us who couldn't ever wade through the Luther volumes. Believe me, I was delighted to see one section labeled "The Church of Sanctification," another "Sanctification is the Work of God," another "Sanctification as the Response of the Justified Sinner," and another "Fruit."

I have been waiting for you to challenge me or even accuse me of confusing sanctification with justification. If I have teetered on the edge of Osiandranism (are you surprised that I know about the bitter controversy between Luther and Osiander??), it is only because I am not a theologian and do not pretend to be! I hold with Luther (if I understand him rightly!) that justification is an act of God for us human beings, and sanctification is the process of growing in grace and holiness, the response in the justified sinner to the boundless grace of God. I am also happy to see that he did not cast out the saints, only the misuse of saints.

Yes, I have a Catholic calendar, which I follow with great interest because, yes, I do love the saints! And we are rapidly approaching All Saints' Day, which is still in the Protestant liturgical calendar, although our practice of it is often ignored because of Reformation Day. And it is not even noted on a calendar sent me by a Protestant organization I will not name. The Catholic calendar is filling up with saints as we approach All Saints' Day—Father Damian, the Belgian priest whose fruit of the gift was to bring the Gospel to the lepers on the island of Molakai, and finally could address them as Fellow-Sufferers because he himself had contracted the dreaded disease. St. Francis, whose fruit was to teach us that imitating Christ is not only possible but is an adventure. St. Jerome, whose fruit was translating the Bible into Latin and then into the vernacular. A scholar and a shaper of language!

Fruits, Tate! How can we get the Church we love to foster the growth of the holiness fruit of the gift in us ordinary folk?

As ever,

Molly

P.S. Incidentally, St. Jerome loved to write letters—long ones!

Dear Martha,

Forgive me, Martha, but I simply had to laugh aloud when I read your account of how, after the excellent discussion, your Bible study collapsed into a jeremiad on the present generation! I use the word "jeremiad" advisedly because it comes from the prophet Jeremiah, who is supposed to have written the book of Lamentations, a catalog of disappointment and complaints about the godlessness of the Israelites and everyone else under the sun. If it is any comfort, Martha, the saints, too, at times spoke and wrote jeremiads. I have been reading about St. Jerome, who lived through the fall of his beloved city Rome to the barbarians in the year 410 A.D. With disillusionment and disgust he had seen the Christian society in Rome become as decadent and luxury loving as pagan society, so much so it was hard to tell the difference between them.

Jeremiah was a gentle, loving man. Was he silent when he saw the godlessness of the kingdom of Judah? No! Indeed, he was commanded by God "to tear up and to knock down, to destroy and overthrow"—but also, please note, "to build and to plant." Was Jerome silent when he saw the godlessness of both Christians and pagans in Rome? No! He spoke against the disintegration he saw around him, but, please note, he also translated the Scripture he loved with a passion into a language that could reach the heart. Should we be silent when we see sin prevail in a world that denies the existence of sin? No, but our creative energy and effort should not go into denunciation but into bringing the new life that is in Christ into the pagan world. Or, as Kierkegaard tongue-in-cheekily put it, reintroducing Christianity into Christendom.

Instead of asking why young people do not go to church and

104

denouncing them for it, perhaps it would be more appropriate to ask: Why is the Church not drawing young people through its doors to worship the one true God? Church seems to them to lack spiritual virility. Could it be because they are seeking something radical and revolutionary and the Church is offering them a God who is so nice and a Christianity so sweet that they are nauseated. Whether they know it or not, they crave something rigorous and demanding, not the "incarnate niceness of God." Or can it be that we Christian adults have made them see the Church as the guardian of morality? The moment young people perceive the Church as the guardian of morality, they see the Church as an enemy. If they suffer a mild attack of moral despair, they would rather not go to the Church for help but to the professions whose members are not moralists. They seem to feel that doctors, psychiatrists, and social workers are more expert in the complexities of personality than we church members with our correct Christian principles.

On the other hand, Martha, could young people be staying away from church because it proclaims a love that is alarmingly different from the natural love they know? Repelled by the love that is symbolized by a Cross, they go seeking for an elusive happiness in other religions. The task of the Church, it seems to me, is to show them that only when they surrender to what repels them can they discover the joy in it. —Anyway, whatever it is about the Church that fails to draw young people to church, we had better find out what it is and do something about it! Why? Because we are the Church!

Love,

Molly

P.S. It's the Festival Day of St. Francis of Assisi today. He knew how to draw young people to the Cross! They came in flocks to follow the Way of the Cross because they saw Francis himself doing it and blessing every thornbush, rock, and pain along the way.

Dear Molly,

We had our Bible study last night, and I think everyone repented of how we ended two weeks ago. I read your letter, and one of the women sighed, "She makes my mind ache!" Someone said, "Maybe it's our spirits that ache. Maybe there's such a thing as growing pains of the spirit." I had brought along your letter to me written on May 15, in which you called a childish faith a tra-la-la Christianity. The disillusionment that is sure to come if our eyes are at all open you called living in the Land of Ish.

The land on the other side of the Kingdom of Tra-la-la and the Land of Ish you called the Kingdom of the Second Spontaneity, where we live like a child in the joy of forgiveness and freedom in Christ. I read the letter to them and we discussed it, and then we read those little love letters of John's at the end of the New Testament. It was wonderful!

I bet you are asking, "And what did you all talk about over coffee and brownies, when women as a rule descend from 'lofty talk' to chatter and gossip?" I think if you had been present and we had done just that, you would have steered us to the question: Why do people find happiness in other people's misfortunes or faults or failures?

But we did not descend to gossip, Molly. We talked about the Church. My sister-in-law tried to steer us on the negative road by asking why preachers do not preach our hearts to overflowing as they once did. She remembers sitting between her mother and father in church and wondering why they were dabbing at their eyes with handkerchiefs and why the preacher was stopping to take off his glasses and wipe his face and then his glasses. Someone else in the group said, "Thank God preachers don't preach congregations to tears anymore! Think of the cost of providing boxes of kleenex as well as hymn books in every hymn rack!"—But here comes my open-closet question!

Is it morbid to feel emotional about one's faith?

Here's another question! Aren't we supposed to feel bound together in a "communion" in church? Most of the time I go to church and sit in my pew as an "I." I go to the Lord's Supper as an "I." I go home again as an "I." I don't always feel like a "communion of saints"!

Thank you, Molly, for letting me be my true self with you! Yesterday, while I stood waiting for Mr. Kuhlman to sign some letters, I looked down at his head with its short, thick gray hair and wondered what was happening in there. At the same time I thought that he did not have any notion at all what was happening inside <u>my</u> head. Are we really and truly a "communion of saints," Molly?

Love,

Martha

Dear Molly,

Legend has it that our saint today was a pupil of St. John and was ordained by the Apostle Peter. It is not legend but fact that he lived in the time of the tremendous growth of the Christian Church. Origen wrote, "Christians saw amazing sights and wonders then." Christianity was forbidden by Roman law, so there were lots of martyrs. Was there a great spurt of growth every time there was a spurt of martyrs' blood? Ignatius was thrown to the wild beasts to provide entertainment for the crowds at the amphitheater in Rome. On his way there from Antioch, a condemned man, he wrote something I will quote to you because you grind wheat and make bread: "I am God's wheat and I am ground by the teeth of wild beasts that I may be found pure bread."

I am sure, Molly, that you do not want "then, oh then!" back again. You wish growth in the Church you and I love—and not just the growth that comes by uniting synods. 2 + 2 will always equal 4, but 2 + 2 does not necessarily equal 4 fruit-bearing Christians, and that, it seems, is what you profoundly and passionately want. Molly, dear Molly, the Christian Church's branches are loaded with the fruit of the Holy Spirit—fruit-bearing Christians. Sure, they drop off in death. We hear the plop when the fruit falls, and we sigh, "Ah, there dropped another saint!" Last week I attended the funeral of a beautiful fruit-of-the-Spirit. For years she was a cook in a home for mentally retarded persons in our town. They were all there, her friends, with all their emotions showing. Joy in having known her, sorrow at her leaving them behind, and pure radiant joy when the pastor spoke of the heavenly home to which she had gone.

In your last letter you asked, "How can we get the Church

we love to foster the growth of fruit?" Did you forget for a moment that <u>we</u> are the Church, that <u>we</u> are the communion of saints? Or is the "communion of saints" a big lie invented by the Church hierarchy to establish its presence and power in the world? Are there only "I"'s in the Church? Is there no "We"?

Please do not think that I am pontificating, Molly, but you have helped me so much in your letters, more than I can tell you. So may I humbly try to help you on this question of "I" and "We" and "the communion of saints"? This letter may get long, but bear with me!

It is not the Church or its doctrines and rituals that determine the "We." Nor is it the individual's relation to the Church that determines it, or for that matter determines the relationship of the "I" to God. It is the relationship to God that determines the relationship to the Church, determines the We, determines the communion of saints, determines whether the communion of saints is a "communion of indifferent existences" (Søren K. said that. I read it in his Journals last night. He rightly calls that paganism). The stronger the relationship to God, the stronger the We. The closer the I becomes in the relationship to God, the more related the I becomes in the We, in the communion of saints. If you can stand another equation from me, here it is:

The more of Thee
in me
the greater in me
the We.

So the real questions are: What fosters the single individual's relationship to God? How does one become increasingly Christian when one is already a Christian? How does one lay hold of the power that builds a strong relationship to God? Through the Holy Spirit, of course, but we must not forget the Word, the Sacraments, Prayer.

110

Molly, do you passionately love the Word? Last night I was reading that passionate poet John Donne and found something I immediately copied into my own journal to pass on to you. Here it is:

> My God, my God, Thou art a direct God, may I not say a literal God, a God that wouldest be understood literally, and according to the plain sense of all that thou sayest? But thou art also a figurative, a metaphorical God too; a God in whose words there is such a height of figures, such voyages, such peregrinations to fetch remote and precious metaphors, such extensions, such spreadings, such Curtains of Allegories, such third Heavens of Hyperboles, such harmonious elocutions. O, what words but thine can express the inexpressible texture and composition of thy word.

Molly, do you passionately pray? Yes, I know that prayer is a very private matter, but it bears its fruit in public.

Lest I fall into the sin of talking <u>about,</u> about patient, persevering reading of the Word even when the hunger temporarily is not there, and <u>about</u> patient, persevering prayer even when we feel too busy or when God seems to be too busy and is not listening, I shall stop right now!

Truly yours,

Tate

October 23

Dear Soul Surgeon,

Ouch!

I know that surgery is performed with a scalpel, not a pea-
cock feather, but your scalpel was very sharp and cut very deep.
Therefore I will admit myself into the intensive care unit of
Mt. Carmel on Lake Carlos near Alexandria, Minnesota, next
Friday and place my soul in the care of a staff of highly recom-
mended spiritual therapists for a long weekend ending, quite fit-
tingly, on All Saints' Day.

Your dis-eased patient,

Molly

Dear Martha,

No, Martha, we who are baptized in the one Spirit are not loners. We are not solitary hikers on the road of sanctification, on the way to becoming what we already are in Christ. We are hiking along with a host of fellow-hikers, authentic "I"s, redeemed and brought into relationship to God. Saints, all of us, be we radiant saints whose sanctity shines, or saints who stammer and stumble and fall and will fall again and again and yet again. Nevertheless, Martha, we are a communion of saints—or redeemed sinners, if you prefer, and are still clinging to the wrong concept of saints as holy, pure, and perfect!

I myself have had to grow into the concept of the communion of saints. I confess that I used to sit in the back pew in church where I usually sit, watch people come down from the communion table, and think unkind thoughts about certain people whose worthiness to go to the Lord's table I doubted. Then I read something Luther said about saints sharing each other's burdens and blessings, and the thought hit me that our burdens as well as our blessings bind us together. After that I found myself looking at my fellow-saints coming down from the communion table with different eyes. With sanctified eyes, Martha!

The middle-aged matron with a long and debilitating disease—her patience in suffering flows into me. That woman whose favorite sport is shredding reputations. Her burden is feeling as if she has no value, so she makes herself feel better by discrediting the value of others. Her burden is mine to share, and my prayer for her flows out to her. That almost painfully humble professor of religion—his humility flows into me and blesses me. As they process down the aisle, all these saints alive, and as their blessings and burdens flow into me, I silently and secretly tilt my own halo to them. We are, bless the Holy Trinity, we are what we are called to be—saints alive!

Next Friday, Martha, I am going to a long weekend retreat at Mt. Carmel. It ends on All Saints' Day. Tell me if either or neither or both of your churches celebrate that day. Protestants as a rule do not <u>celebrate</u> it. We may stand in silence for a minute in memory of the members who have died within the past year and whose names may be listed in the church bulletin. That, in my opinion, is not celebrating all the saints!

Love,

Molly

November 2
All Souls' Day

Dear Tate,

Home again to my daily life. Nothing has changed. Emma woke me as usual at seven with her thumping tail and deep-throated love sounds and offered me one of my shoes. Ole brought me his morning offering, one of the mice that move in every fall when the weather gets nippy. And nippy it is! The furnace kicks on with an alarming sound and reminds me that way last spring I was planning to call the furnace man about it. —So nothing has changed, Tate, and yet everything has changed!

Did you suspect that I was a bit nervous about going to a retreat? A Protestant retreat, that is. What would "they" do? Subject me to religious gimmickry? I despise it! Teach me techniques of prayer? I hate techniques of anything! Cultivate "interpersonal relationships" by way of touching and hugging? Something within me requires the touching of hearts first and foremost. —May I assure you that there was nothing at all of what I feared at Mt. Carmel. The directors, Johann and Sonja Hinderlie, and the staff for the week, the elder Hinderlies, Carroll and Mary, and Sister Miriam, a Catholic nun, are no fonder of spiritual stroking and manipulation than I am.

Thank you for making me face up to the weakness of my prayer life and asking those painful questions that sent me to Mt. Carmel. You must have sensed that my praying did not add up to much more than frightened petitions if one of my loved ones was in trouble or sleepy petitions as I lay snuggled in bed. You must have known that I experienced the noise and static of vagrant thoughts and that it was hard for me to hold my attention to praying for even ten minutes. (And St. Paul admonished us to "pray without ceasing!"). That was my "speaking with God"! Yet I could find time to speak with friends in letters, with you, for example, and love every minute of it! So was God really not

115

my friend, then? If I could not or would not speak with God in prayer, was I really living my life as a friend of God?

I cannot boast that I came back to my daily life a fervent and untiring prayer, but, thanks be to God and my mentors at Mt. Carmel, things fell into place. All eight of them (counting Holy Trinity as Three!) helped me to recognize some of the fears and misunderstandings that had made me shy away from praying: a fear of making God into the Head of a Heavenly Welfare Agency, an aversion to telling God what he certainly already knew, and a reluctance to turn him into someone whose mind I had to change.—Perhaps I should say "All nine of them," for there was a retreatant from somewhere out East who also proved to be a disentangler of some knotty thoughts.

There were only six of us retreatants, which gave us much solitude, much time to be with mentors on a one-to-one basis, to walk and talk together in twos or threes. Lots of time and opportunity to meditate and pray alone—or together. I have never been able to pray together with adults, Tate, but I found that I could do it with a deep sense of communion at Mt. Carmel. Amazingly enough, with that complete stranger from somewhere out East!

The knottiest knot that was unkinked at Mt. Carmel—can you guess it, Tate? Have you guessed that in and under my obvious reverence for saints and martyrs there was a guilt that I was not like them, that I was not imitating them? Guilt because I did not practice any of that penitential stuff, I did not fast, I did not walk barefoot on sharp stones, I did not shut myself in a hermit cell and meditate and pray for forty-eight hours without sleeping. Guilt because I did not want even a twentieth-century modified and mitigated version of that Middle ages mode of penance.—Well, I retain the reverence for those saints, but I am liberated from that guilt, and that is what I meant when I said that nothing has changed in my daily life, but everything has changed!

116

Prayer does not necessarily need a time and a place. I do not have to build a log hut in the woodlot where I can go to find silence and solitude. I do not need to convert a room in my house into a chapel. I do not need to fence in hours of the day or night as "devotional hours." My heart is my hut, my hermit cell, my chapel, my house of prayer, and God, who laughs at time—indeed, has eternalized it—meets me there in his eternal now. My everyday life is full of little solitudes and silences—even when I'm running my aging vacuum cleaner—or running my aging body on my four-mile daily lap. I need silence and solitude and prayer far more than those hermits of old, but I do not have to isolate myself or torture my body to have God reveal the mystery of himself to me. Or reveal the mystifications of my own self to me!

I can't quite explain this new and amazing gift of prayer abiding in me and me abiding in prayer. How I wish we could talk as I was able to talk with that retreatant from the East!

Do you know that Carmel is a Hebrew word meaning "a fruitful place"? The Elijah-fruit on Mt. Carmel in Israel was monotheism firmly established. The Molly-fruit at Mt. Carmel in Alexandria was the gift of being able to abide in prayer and have prayer abide in—Molly! As well as a brighter vision of grace and effort walking joyfully hand-in-hand. Companions, Tate, along the road of sanctification! Please note, Sir, the road of sanctification, not the road to sanctification!

> Grace and peace!
>
> Molly

November 2
All Souls' Day

Dear Molly,

Will you marry me?

Love,

Tate

118

Dear Tate,

Our letters crossed!

All Souls' Day is not April Fools' Day. You would not have the heart to play games with me on All Souls' Day!! No, of course not!

If only your letter had come October 5, or before I went off to Mt. Carmel! My response would have been a fervent YES. But you now have my letter written on November 2, and you now know of the existence of "another man"!! He may never write to me. I may never see him again. But if he does write, if I do see him again, then—oh, Tate, I'm as confused as a teenage girl who is not sure which lover she loves! I truly have fallen in love with you through your letters, and I truly do not care whether or not you are thick or thin, hairy or hairless, energetic or lethargic! But—there is this man I met at the retreat—! Please let me "abide" in your love for a while until I get my bearings!

> Love—oh, yes, yes!
> But marry you??
> Can you wait for my answer?
>
> Molly

Dear Molly,

Would it help if I tell you that "the other man" and I are one
and the same man?

Love,

Tate

P.S. BOTH of them now ask:
Molly, will you marry me?

Dear Tate!

You rogue! You imposter!! You schemer!!! No, I will not marry
you! Absolutely not!! Except—perhaps—on one condition—! If
mh, your secretary will consent to be my maid of honor. Ask
her!

Love, enough for two of you!

Molly

November 14

Dearest Molly,

Mr. Kuhlman just asked me to be matron of honor at your
wedding!

YesYesYesYesYesYesYesYesYesYesYesYesYesYesYesYes!

OH, YES!

Love,
Martha

122